Activity Book 4

Comprehension and Skill Work

Units 21–25

Cambium
LEARNING®
Group

Voyager
LEARNING

ISBN-13: 978-1-60218-567-8
ISBN-10: 1-60218-567-0
167177/6-13

Printed in the United States of America

Published and Distributed by

17855 Dallas Parkway, Suite 400 • Dallas, TX 75287 • 800 547-6747
www.voyagerlearning.com

PHOTO AND ILLUSTRATION CREDITS

1, 4, 9, 27: Abraham Lincoln ©Library of Congress. 1, 2, 8: Lincoln's cabin Public Domain. 1, 16: Buffalo ©istockphoto.com/Michael Thompson, covered wagon train ©Clipart.com, train engine ©Clipart.com, 1, 17: Betsy's new home illustrated by Wilson Ong. 3: Lincoln Memorial ©Jupiter Images. 3, 6, 8: "Abraham Learns" illustrated by Larry Johnson. 4: Abraham Lincoln and Mary Todd ©Library of Congress. 14, 17, 19, 21, 26, 30, 31, 41, 63. 64, 68, 70, 83, 85, 92: Illustrated by Eldon Doty. 15, 22: Thomas Edison ©Hulton Archive/Getty Images. 16. Baby ©Library of Congress. 16, 27: Phonograph ©Library of Congress. 27: Railroad workers ©Jupiter Images. 33: Illustrated by Ashley Mims. 34: Penguin illustrations ©istockphoto.com. 37: Penguins (top left to bottom right) ©Punchstock, ©Kim Westerskov/Getty Images, ©DLILLC/Corbis, ©istockphoto.com/ Stephan Zabel. 39: ©J. David Andrews/Corbis. 40: ©istockphoto.com. 42-43: Illustrated by Neal Sharp. 45: Harpy eagle ©Punchstock, howler monkey ©istockphoto.com/Eric Delmar. 72-82, 86: Illustrated by Janet Pedersen. 71, 87, 90: Cover illustration ©1997 by John Steven Gurney from "The Absent Author (A to Z #1)" by Ron Roy. Published by arrangement with Random House Children's Books, a division of Random House, Inc. 87, 90: "Arthur's Pet Business" by Marc Brown ©1990 by Marc Brown. Cover used by permission of Little Brown & Company Books for Young Readers. 87, 90: Cover illustration ©1992 by Sal Murdocca from "Dinosaurs Before Dark" ©1992 by Mary Pope Osborne. Published by arrangement with Random House Children's Books, a division of Random House, Inc. 87, 90: "Flat Stanley" by Jeff Brown and illustrated by Tomi Ungerer, ©1964. Cover courtesy of Harper Trophy/Harper Collins Publishers, Inc. 87, 90: "Judy Moody Saves the World." Text ©2001 by Megan McDonald. Illustrations ©2001 by Peter H. Reynolds. Reproduced by permission of the publisher Candlewick Press, Inc., Cambridge, MA. 87: Cover illustration ©1989 by Bruce Degan from "The Magic School Bus Inside the Human Body" by Joanne Cole. Reprinted by permission of Scholastic Inc. 87: "Time for Kids: Thomas Edison" by Time Inc. ©2005 by Time Inc. Used by permission of HarperCollins Publishers. Cover: U.S. Department of the Interior, NPS, Edison National Historic Site.

Table of Contents

Unit 25

Written Assessments

Abraham Lincoln:

by

Dear Parents: Ask your child about each event on the timeline. Congratulate your child for being a historian.

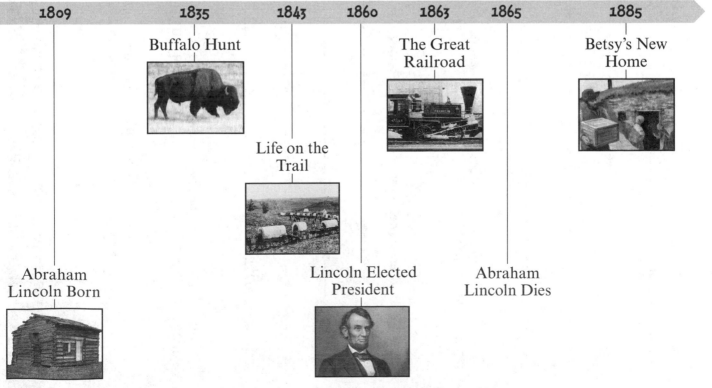

| 1809 | 1835 | 1843 | 1860 | 1863 | 1865 | 1885 |

Buffalo Hunt

The Great Railroad

Betsy's New Home

Life on the Trail

Abraham Lincoln Born

Lincoln Elected President

Abraham Lincoln Dies

Teachers: If you are using the Activity Book, tear out and staple pages 1–4 to make a separate mini-book.

Simple Beginnings

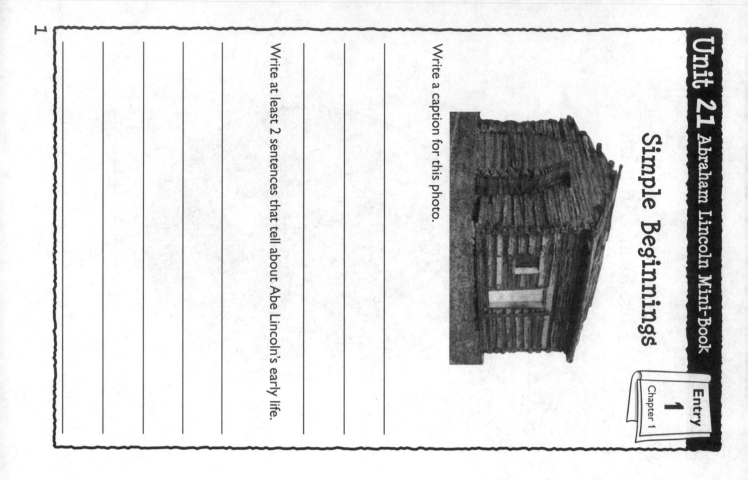

Write a caption for this photo.

_____

_____

Write at least 2 sentences that tell about Abe Lincoln's early life.

_____

_____

_____

_____

_____

1

Your Opinion: Do you think Lincoln was a great man?
Why or why not? Write at least 2 sentences

I think Lincoln _____ a great man because
           was   was not

_____

_____

Your Opinion: Would you have voted for Lincoln? Why or why not?

I _____ _____ have voted for Lincoln
 would   would not

because _____

_____

_____

6

Abraham Learns

Write a caption for this illustration.

_____

_____

Write at least 2 sentences that tell about Abraham Lincoln as a young boy.

_____

_____

_____

2

Lincoln, Remembered

Write a caption for this photo.

_____

_____

5

Lincoln, the Man

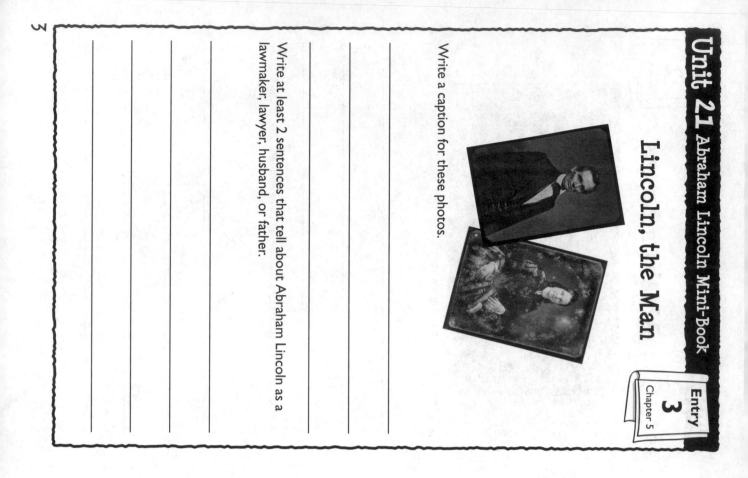

Write a caption for these photos.

_____

_____

Write at least 2 sentences that tell about Abraham Lincoln as a lawmaker, lawyer, husband, or father.

_____

_____

_____

_____

_____

Lincoln, the President

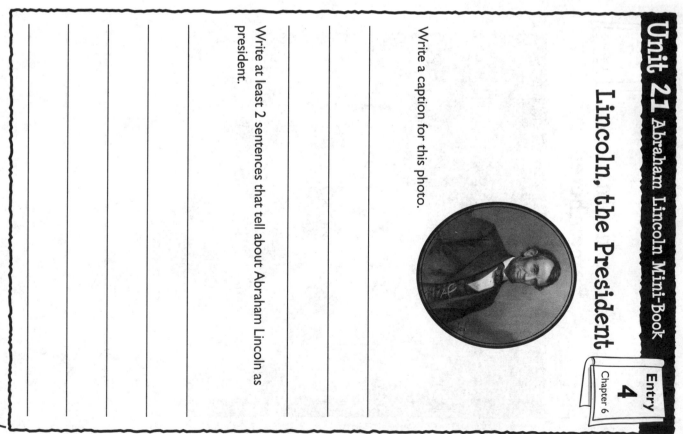

Write a caption for this photo.

_____

_____

Write at least 2 sentences that tell about Abraham Lincoln as president.

_____

_____

_____

_____

_____

Unit 21 Activity 1
Use after Exercise 1, Introduction, and Chapter 1

Name _____

Story Comprehension
Introduction

1 **A biography is the story of a real person's life. A biography is . . .**

○ fiction.   ○ nonfiction.

2 **Many stories have been written about Abraham Lincoln because he is an important person in history.**

Check three things that tell he was an important person in history.

___ His face is on United States money—pennies and five dollar bills.

___ He lived in a log cabin.

___ A memorial was built in his honor.

___ People in the United States celebrate his birthday every February.

3 **Abraham Lincoln has inspired many people. He worked hard to make the world a better place.**

List three things that you learned about him in Chapter 1.

- _____

- _____

- _____

4 **Write two questions that you have about Abraham Lincoln.**

You may wish to start with *Who, What, Where, When, How,* or *Why.*

- _____

  _____

- _____

  _____

Unit 21 Activity 2

Name _____

Story Comprehension • Locating Information
Young Abraham

Locate and complete the information about Abraham Lincoln. If you need to, look in your storybook.

Pages 17 and 18

1 **Abraham worked hard as a young child. List two things he did.**

- _____

- _____

Pages 18 and 19

2 **Abraham loved to learn. List two ways Abraham learned new things.**

- _____

- _____

Maze Reading

When you come to the words between the parentheses, circle the word that makes the most sense in the paragraph. Then reread the paragraph to see if it makes sense.

When Abraham Lincoln was young, he worked hard. He helped to build his family's (brick, log, talk) cabin, and he worked in the (office, fields, sad). When he was nine years old, (its, over, his) mother died. It was a sad (time, only, book). Later, his father remarried a kind-hearted (many, widow, man), and the family was happy again.

(Old, Abraham's, Minnie Bird's) new mother encouraged him to read (or, and, talk) learn. Abraham loved to learn. He learned by reading books and talking to others.

Unit 21 Activity 3
Use after Exercise 3 and Chapters 4 and 5

Name _____

Story Comprehension • Cause and Effect
Learning by Littles

Locate and complete the information about Abraham Lincoln. If you need to, look in your storybook.

Pages 26 and 27

Cause and Effect: When something happens, it often makes something else happen.

Cause • Event		Effect • What Happened?
When Lincoln got a job on a flatboat, he saw people being sold as slaves.	→	Seeing the slaves made Abe feel _____
Lincoln treated others well and told funny stories.	→	People _____ _____
Lincoln practiced making speeches.	→	He learned to _____ _____

Vocabulary

1 **Lincoln loved books, but they were too** _____ **to buy.**

   ○ expensive   ○ pretty   ○ cheap

2 **Lincoln thought important people** _____

   ○ were tall   ○ were educated   ○ couldn't read

3 **Lincoln felt slavery was wrong. That was his** _____

   ○ gift   ○ job   ○ opinion

Unit 21 Optional Activity
Use anytime after Exercise 4 and Chapter 4

Name _____

Passage Reading Fluency

1. Practice these words:

general	honest	discovered	money	integrity	woman

2. Read the passage 2 times. Cross out a log cabin each time you read the story.

Honest Abe

Like many great leaders, Abraham Lincoln was a person of integrity.   11
He tried to do what was right. He did his very best at everything he did.   27
He was honest and respectful.   32

There are many stories about Abraham Lincoln's integrity. When   41
he was a young man, he worked in a general store. Once, when he was   56
counting the cash, he found that he had charged someone a few extra   69
pennies. He closed the store and walked a long way to return the money.   83
Abe did what was right.   88

Another time, Abe discovered that he did not give a woman enough   100
tea for what she paid. Much to the woman's surprise, Abe took more tea   114
to her. The woman didn't even know she was missing it. She was so   128
impressed with Abe's honesty that she   134
invited him in for a cup of tea. Abe did   144
what was right.   147

Abraham Lincoln was an   151
ordinary man who became great.   156
He has inspired leaders all over   162
the world to do what they think   169
is right.   171

3. Set a timer and see how far you can read in one minute.
   Then cross out the timer.

Unit 21 Activity 4
Use after Exercise 4 and Chapter 6

Name _____

Characterization • Lincoln, the President

1 Complete the web by writing words that describe Abraham Lincoln.

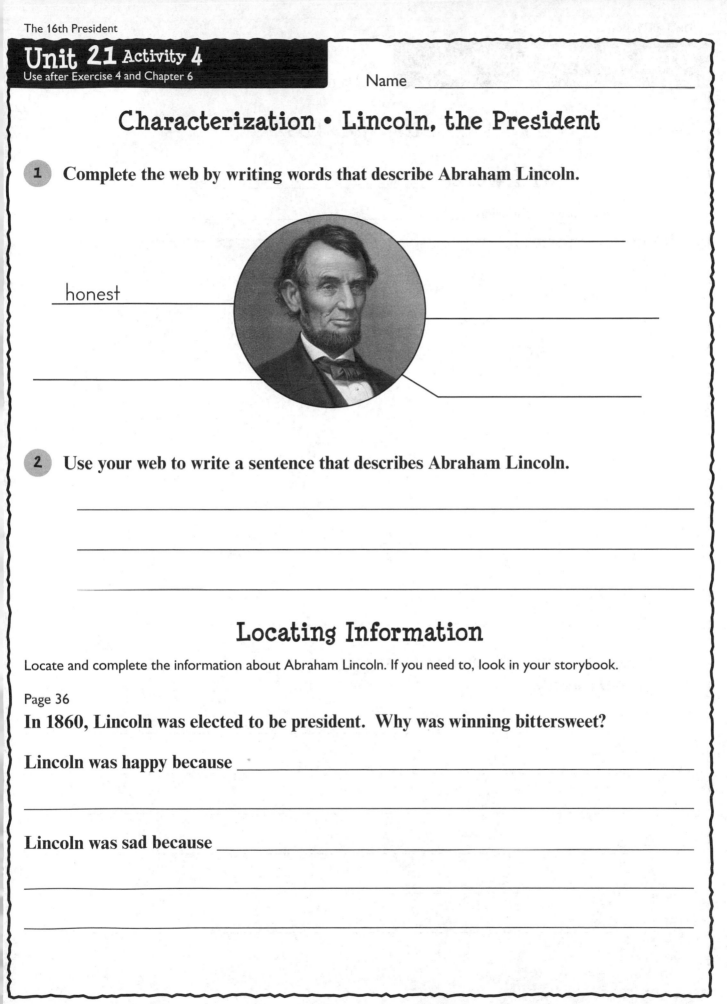

honest

2 Use your web to write a sentence that describes Abraham Lincoln.

_____

_____

_____

Locating Information

Locate and complete the information about Abraham Lincoln. If you need to, look in your storybook.

Page 36

In 1860, Lincoln was elected to be president. Why was winning bittersweet?

Lincoln was happy because _____

_____

Lincoln was sad because _____

_____

_____

Unit 21 Just for Fun
Use anytime after Chapter 6

Name _____

Just for Fun

If I were _____ . . .

Draw a picture of yourself as _____

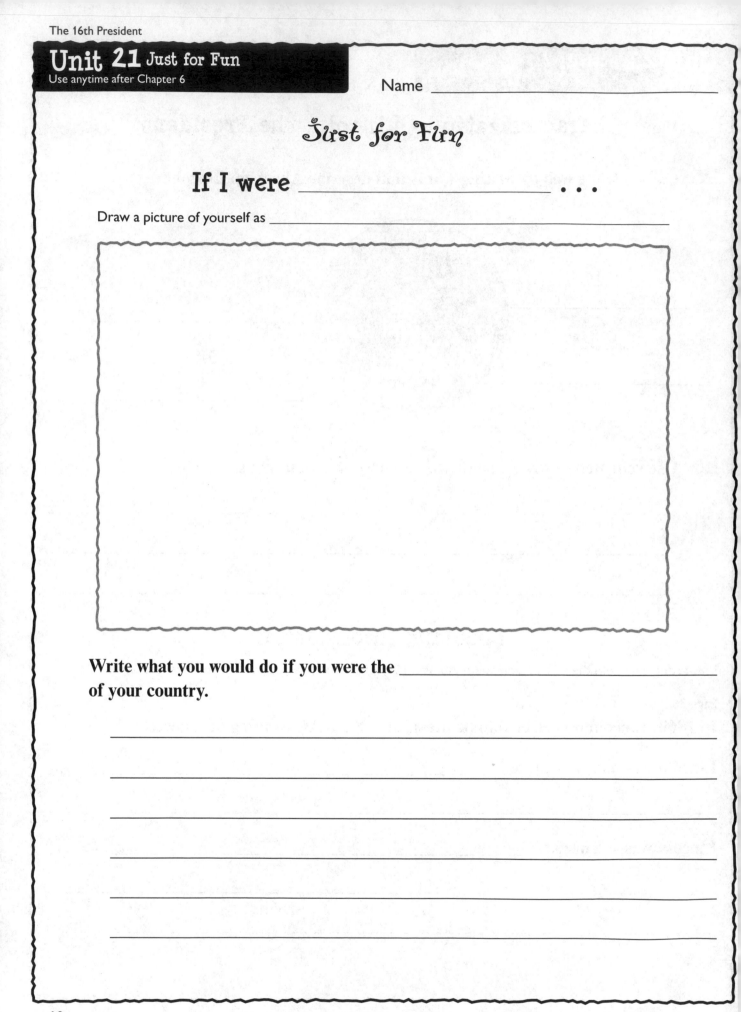

Write what you would do if you were the _____
of your country.

_____

_____

_____

_____

_____

_____

Unit 22 Activity 1
Use after Exercise 1 and Chapter 1

Name _____

Passage Comprehension
Let There Be Light

1 *Thomas Edison: A Brilliant Inventor* **is . . .**

    ○ a legend.   ○ a biography.   ○ a tall tale.

2 **Is a biography fiction or nonfiction?**   fiction   nonfiction

3 **Why did <u>thousands of people</u> go to Menlo Park on December 31, 1879?**

Thousands of people went to Menlo Park to see Edison's _____

_____

4 **Biographies are written about inspiring, interesting, or famous people.**

Lincoln is inspiring because he was _____

_____

Edison is inspiring because he was _____

_____

5 **Asking Questions: What I Want to Learn About Thomas Edison.**
Write one question you want answered about Thomas Edison.
Start your question with one of these words: *Who, What, When, Where, Why, How.*

_____

_____

_____

_____

Unit 22 Activity 2
Use after Exercise 1 and Chapter 1

Name _____

Fact Summary
Let There Be Light

1 **Something that is practical is . . .**

    ○ funny.   ○ easy to use.   ○ hard to use.

2 **Write facts that tell about the kind of lighting there was before Edison invented a practical lightbulb.** If you need to, look in your book on pages 1 and 2.

> **Topic/Main Idea:** Lighting was not practical before Edison's lightbulb.

Fact 1 (page 1)
- Oil or gas lamps started fires.

Fact 2 (page 1)
- Oil or gas lamps

  _____

  _____

Fact 3 (page 2)
- Lightbulbs were too bright and hurt people's eyes.

Fact 4 (page 2)
- Lightbulbs

  _____

  _____

  _____

3 **Using at least three of the facts listed above, write a paragraph about the lighting that people used before Edison invented a practical lightbulb.**

Lighting before Edison's lightbulb was not very practical. _____

_____

_____

_____

_____

Unit 22 Activity 3
Use after Exercise 2 and Chapter 2

Name _____

Passage Comprehension
Little Al's Boyhood

1 **Cause and Effect:** Al was a very curious boy. Complete the chart to show what Al did to try to understand how things worked.

Al's Question		What Al Did		Outcome
Can I hatch goose eggs?	➡	_____ _____ _____	➡	_____ _____ _____

Al's Question		What Al Did		Outcome
How do birds fly?	➡	_____ _____ _____	➡	_____ _____ _____

2 **Personal Response:** Would you have wanted to be young Thomas Edison's friend? Why or why not?
Use at least one snazzy word.

Snazzy Words
brilliant
creative
curious
experiment
daydream

I _____ have wanted to be
      would   would not

Edison's friend because _____

_____

_____

_____

_____

Unit 22 Activity 4
Use after Exercise 2 and Chapter 2

Name _____

Compare and Contrast

How was Al's childhood the same as or different from yours?

What	Al	You
Electricity	• had no electricity	• have electricity
Learned to read	• at home	• _____
Loved to read about	• science and history	• _____ _____ _____

Timeline Cover and Entry 1 • Following Directions

1 **Follow the directions to complete the cover and Timeline Entry 1.**

Check the box as you complete each item.

☐ Write your name on your Thomas Edison Timeline cover.

☐ Find 1847. Trace the line with your pencil to the box labeled "Entry 1." Write: Edison was born on February 11, 1847.

2 **Look at the top row of the timeline. Had the Great Railroad been built when Edison was born?**   yes   no

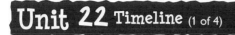
Thomas Edison Timeline
1835-1931

by _____

Teachers: If you are using the Activity Book, tear out and staple pages 15–18 to make a separate Timeline Folder.

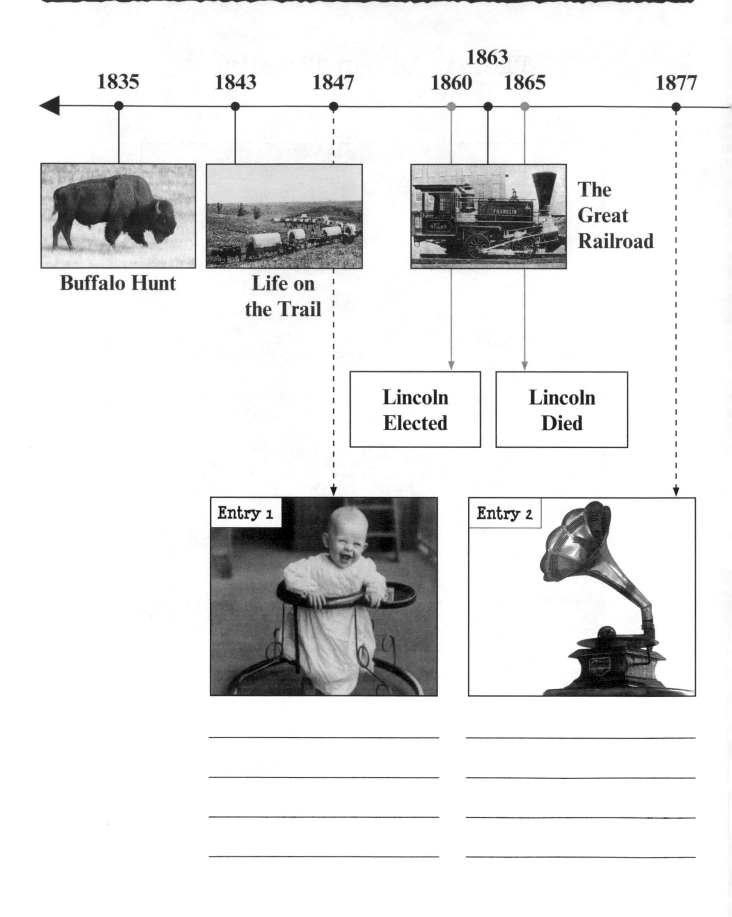

1835   1843   1847   1860   1863   1865   1877

Buffalo Hunt

Life on the Trail

The Great Railroad

Lincoln Elected

Lincoln Died

Entry 1

Entry 2

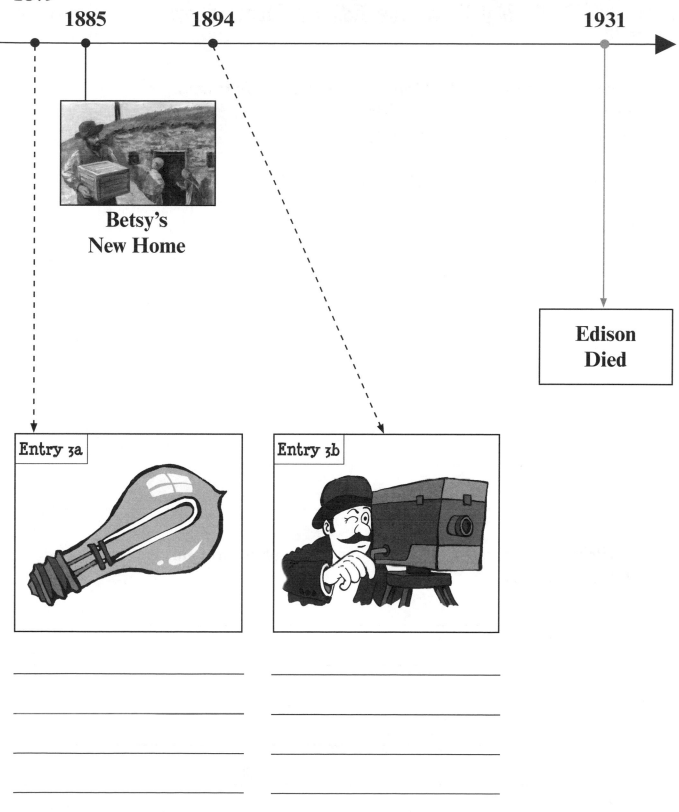

1879

1885

1894

1931

Betsy's
New Home

Edison
Died

Entry 3a

Entry 3b

Entry 4

My Favorite Edison Invention

1. Look through your book, *Thomas Edison: A Brilliant Inventor.*

   What is your favorite invention? _____

2. Draw a picture of your favorite invention.

3. Write a two- or three-sentence caption that explains why this is your favorite Edison invention.

   _____

   _____

   _____

   _____

   _____

Unit 22 Activity 5
Use after Exercise 3 and Chapter 3

Name _____

Passage Reading Fluency

1. Practice these words:

curious	experiments	encouraged	outgrew	imagination

2. Read the story 2 times. Cross out a lightbulb each time you read the story.

Edison, The Boy

When Alva Edison was a boy, people called him Al. Young Al   12
was curious from the time he was little. He asked a lot of questions.   26
Sometimes his imagination got him into trouble, but his parents always   37
encouraged him to ask questions. They liked his spunk!   46

Al was also a hard worker. When he was just twelve years old, he   60
got a job on a train. Al sold newspapers, candy, books, and postcards.   73

As Al grew older, he outgrew his nickname. He wanted people to   85
call him Tom. Tom was always busy. He did not like to sit still. Tom   100
Edison was always thinking. He did experiments. He liked to find   111
ways to make things better.   116

Today, people all over the world enjoy Thomas Alva Edison's   126
inventions. People no longer have to spend their evenings by smelly gas   138
lamps. Thomas Edison was a great man.   145

His inventions   147
changed the world.   150

3. Set a timer and see how far you can read in one minute.
   Then cross out the timer.

Name _____

Passage Comprehension
The Amazing Telegraph

1 A machine that was used long ago to send messages across a wire is the . . .

○ wire phone.　　○ telegraph.　　○ cell phone.

2 The telegraph was invented by . . .

○ Samuel F. B. Morse.　○ Thomas Edison.　○ Sir Henry.

3 Samuel F. B. Morse created a special alphabet made of dashes and dots. This alphabet was used to send messages over the telegraph and is called . . .

○ Morse code.　　○ Edison code.　　○ Sir Winston code.

4 Look at the Morse code chart on the right. Answer the question by figuring out the word that is written in Morse code.

In 1863, what was Thomas Edison's job?

---	.--.	.	.-.	.-	-	---	.-.
1	2	3	4	5	6	7	8

telegraph　 o̲ ___ ___ ___ ___ ___ ___ ___
　　　　　　1　2　3　4　5　6　7　8

A .-	N -.
B -...	O ---
C -.-.	P .--.
D -..	Q --.-
E .	R .-.
F ..-.	S ...
G --.	T -
H	U ..-
I ..	V ...-
J .---	W .--
K -.-	X -..-
L .-..	Y -.--
M --	Z --..

5 Now you try it! Complete the message in Morse code in the box below.

You are . . .

-...	.-.	..	.-..	.-..	..	.-	-.	-
1	2	3	4	5	6	7	8	9

___ ___ ___ ___ ___ ___ ___ ___ ___　 just like Edison.
1　2　3　4　5　6　7　8　9

Unit 22 Activity 7
Use after Exercise 4 and Chapter 4

Name _____

Vocabulary Log

Word	Definition	Sentence	Picture
curious	Someone who is curious wants to know about many things.	Thomas Edison was _____ He asked _____ _____	
brilliant	Someone who is brilliant... _____ _____	_____ _____ _____	
expensive	Something that is expensive... _____ _____	_____ _____ _____	
fascinated	Someone who is fascinated is... _____ _____	_____ _____ _____	

Name _____

Characterization • Thomas Edison

1   **Complete the web by writing words that describe Thomas Edison.**

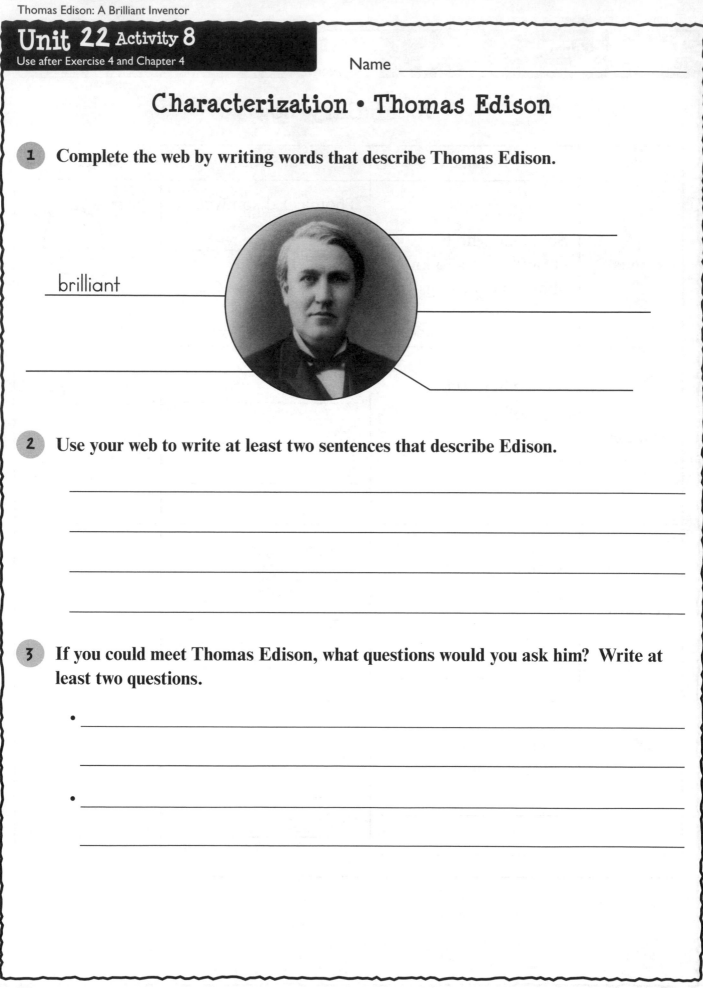

brilliant _____

2   **Use your web to write at least two sentences that describe Edison.**

_____

_____

_____

_____

3   **If you could meet Thomas Edison, what questions would you ask him? Write at least two questions.**

• _____

_____

• _____

_____

Unit 22 Activity 9
Use after Exercise 5 and Chapter 5

Name _____

Passage Reading Fluency

1. Practice these words:

| phonograph | businessmen | answering | machines | favorite |

2. Read the story 2 times. Cross out a phonograph each time you read the story.

Music to the Ears

    Thomas Edison was the first person to record a sound and then   12
play it back. He spoke "Mary had a little lamb" into his new invention   26
and then had his machine "speak" the words back to him. He had   39
invented the phonograph!   42

    At first Edison thought his invention would be most useful for   53
businessmen. They could record their letters instead of writing them   63
down on paper. He also thought the phonograph could be connected   74
to a telephone to record calls, like the answering machines we have now.   87

    He stopped working on the phonograph for about 10 years in order   99
to work on another invention, the lightbulb.   106

    Edison said that the phonograph was his favorite invention because   116
it put music into people's homes.   122

3. Set a timer and see how far you can read in one minute.
   Then cross out the timer.

4. **What is the main idea of the passage?**
   - Edison recorded "Mary Had a Little Lamb."
   - Edison invented the phonograph.
   - Edison invented a better lightbulb.

Name _____

Mystery Person

1 **Who is Mystery Person 1?**

Clue 1: I live in Montgomery, Alabama. I worked as a children's librarian for 30 years.

Clue 2: I just retired from my job as a librarian. I am enjoying traveling. I have visited Ghana and Hilo.

Clue 3: I have a bird named Minnie Bird and a cat named Scraggly Cat.

Who Am I? _____

2 **Who is Mystery Person 2?**

Clue 1: I loved learning and reading.

Clue 2: I was the 16th president of the United States.

Clue 3: My picture is on pennies and five-dollar bills.

Who Am I? _____

Timeline Entry 2 • Following Directions

1 **Look at the top row of the timeline. What was built in 1863?**

In 1863, _____ was built.

2 **Follow the directions to complete Timeline Entry 2.**
Check the box when you complete the item.

☐ Find 1877. Trace the line with your pencil to the box labeled Entry 2. Write the caption: Edison invented the phonograph in 1877.

Unit 22 Activity 11
Use after Exercise 6 and Chapter 6

Name _____

Maze Reading • Passage Comprehension

When you come to the words between the parentheses, circle the word that makes the most sense in the paragraph. Then reread the paragraph to see if it makes sense.

> The filament in a lightbulb gives off light. When the lightbulb was first invented, (the, dug, a) filament that gave off the light (baby, find, did) not last very long. Thomas Edison (worked, dug, dark) on finding a material that would (she, make, go) the lightbulb glow for a long (time, year, many). He tried many different materials, including (linen, goes, dog), grass, tar, horsehair, and human hair. He (glow, went, did) not get discouraged. Finally in October 1879, he used cotton that had been baked in an oven. The lightbulb glowed for 13 hours.

1 **What is a *filament*?**

　　○ a horse　　　　　○ a thin wire or thread　　　○ electricity

2 **Even if he was not successful, Thomas Edison did not get discouraged. Someone who is discouraged . . .**

　　○ doesn't feel good about what they are doing.

　　○ is very curious and excited.

3 **Edison tried to make a filament that would make a lightbulb glow for a long time. Check the materials that he tried.**

　　__ linen　　　　　　__ grass　　　　　　__ human hair

　　__ tar　　　　　　　__ horsehair　　　　__ silk

4 **What material did Edison use for the filament that made the lightbulb burn for 13 hours?**

　　○ linen　　　　　　○ cotton　　　　　　○ grass

Name _____

Diagram • Labeling

Another Bright Idea

Thomas Edison invented a practical lightbulb in 1879.

Look at the diagram of the lightbulb below. Label the parts of the lightbulb.

Word Bank

filament
vacuum
glass
base

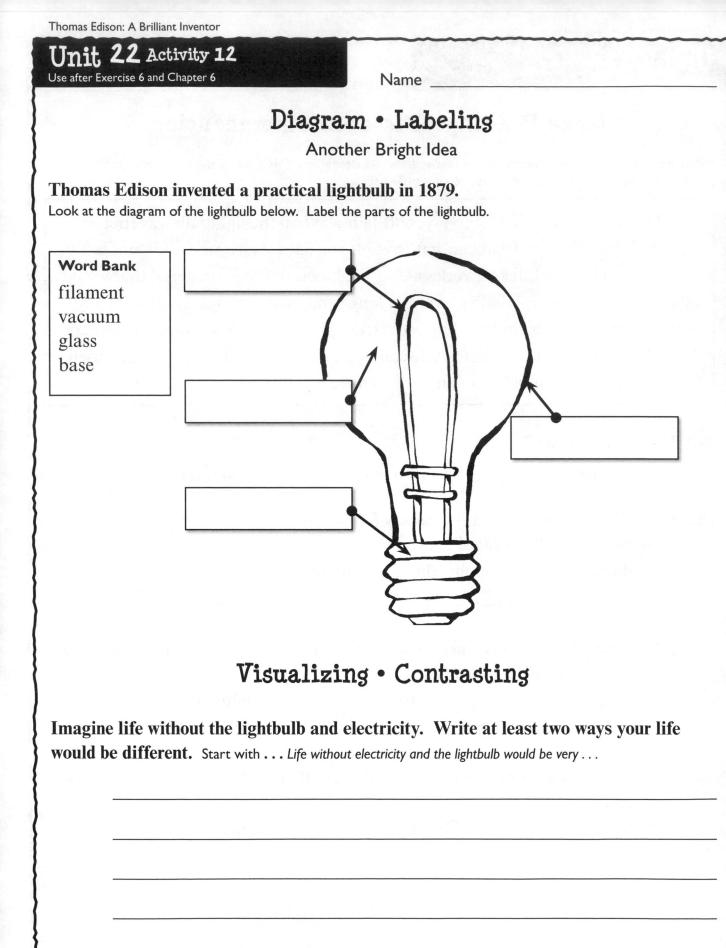

Visualizing • Contrasting

Imagine life without the lightbulb and electricity. Write at least two ways your life would be different. Start with . . . *Life without electricity and the lightbulb would be very . . .*

_____

_____

_____

_____

_____

Unit 22 Activity 13

Name _____

Following Directions
Timeline Entry 3

1 **Look at the top row of the timeline.**
Trace the line from the box with your finger.
When was Lincoln elected?

Lincoln was elected in _____

2 **Look at the top row of the timeline.**
When was the Great Railroad built?

The Great Railroad was built in _____

3 **Find the year 1877. Trace the line to the box**
with your finger. What did Edison invent in 1877?

Edison invented the _____

With this invention, people could

listen to _____

Now people use CD players and other machines.

4 **Check each box when you complete the item.**

☐ Find 1879. Trace the line with your
pencil to the box labeled Entry 3a.
Write the caption: Edison invented the
first practical lightbulb.

☐ Find 1894. Trace the line with your
pencil to the box labeled Entry 3b.
Write the caption: Edison opened the
first motion picture studio.

Unit 22 Just for Fun
Use anytime

Name _____

Just for Fun

You are an inventor! If you invented something, what would it be?

My Invention: _____

By: _____

This is what my invention can do:

_____

_____

_____

_____

_____

___'s

Science Digest

Science and Literature by a Kid

What's Inside

My favorite rain forest animal!

Facts about those cute critters—penguins!

Marvelous Earth!

Teachers: If you are using the Activity Book, tear out and staple pages 29–34 to make a separate mini book.

Our World, Our Home

ARCTIC OCEAN

PACIFIC OCEAN

NORTH AMERICA

ATLANTIC OCEAN

SOUTH AMERICA

EUROPE

AFRICA

ASIA

INDIAN OCEAN

AUSTRALIA

ANTARCTICA

PACIFIC OCEAN

You've traveled with Miss Tam to many places! You know a lot about our world, our home. If you could travel, where in the world would you go? Why?

_____

_____

_____

_____

10

Entry
1b

Table of Contents

Departments

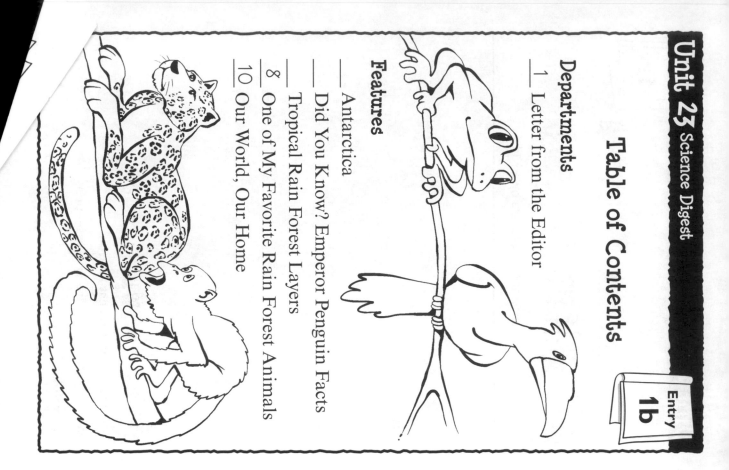

Rain Forest Animals

9

30

Unit 23 Science Digest

Letter From the Editor

Dear Readers,

_____

_____

_____

This Science Digest is about _____

_____

I hope you _____

_____

Sincerely, _____

Unit 23 Science Digest

One of My Favorite

There are many interesting animals in a tropical rain forest. But there is always one that captures your imagination more than the others.

One of my favorite rain forest animals is the

_____

_____

_____

_____

_____

_____

Antarctica

Forest Layers

Facts about each rain forest layer:

Emergent: _____

Canopy: _____

Understory: _____

Forest Floor: _____

Unit 23 Science Digest

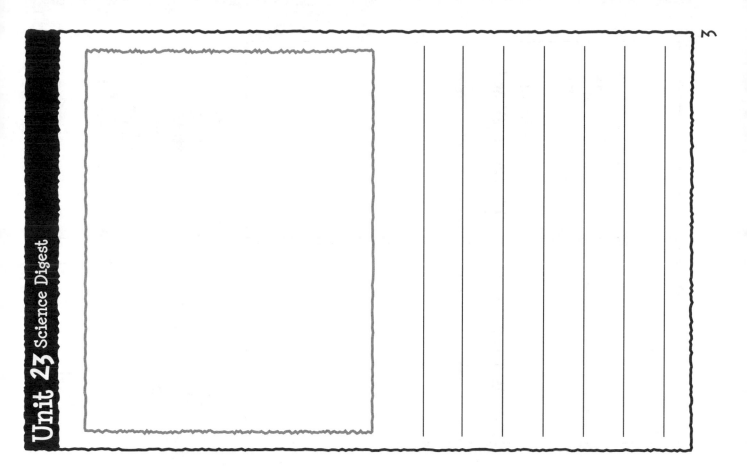

Unit 23 Science Digest

Tropical Rain

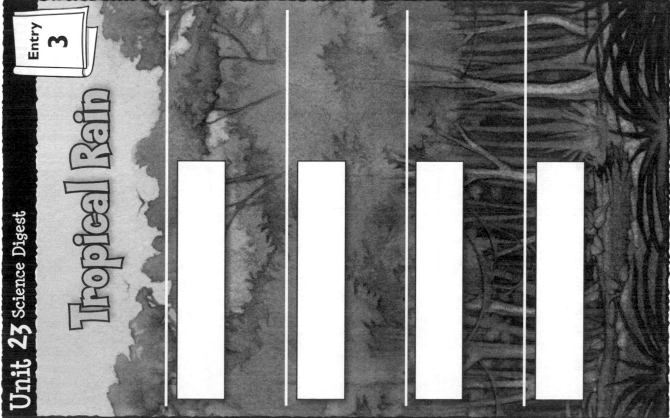

Unit 23 Science Digest

Penguins on the March

Entry
2b

The Antarctic Fall
March, April, May

Adult penguins march
to the rookery.
The females lay eggs
and return to the sea.

The Antarctic Winter
June, July, August

The males take
care of the eggs until
they hatch.

Females return
with food.

Unit 23 Science Digest

Glue the pictures from activity book page 37 into the boxes.
See storybook pages 26 and 27 if you need help.

The Antarctic Spring
September, October, November

Both parents take
turns going to the sea
to eat and taking care
of the babies.

The Antarctic Summer
December, January, February

The young penguins
and their parents leave
the rookery. They go
to the sea to hunt.

Unit 23 Activity 1
Use after Exercise 1 and Antarctica!

Name _____

Fact Summary
Antarctica!

1 **In this article, you learned about the continent of Antarctica.**
Write facts that support the main idea. If you need to, look in your storybook.

> **Topic/Main Idea:** Antarctica is the harshest continent in the world.

Coldest	**Driest**	**Windiest**
❄ thick sheet of ice 7,000 feet deep	❄ _____	❄ _____
❄ 100 degrees below zero in the winter	❄ _____	❄ _____

2 **Using the facts you listed, write a paragraph that tells about Antarctica.**
Start with the main idea. Then choose one favorite fact from each box to explain why Antarctica is the harshest continent in the world.

_____

_____

_____

_____

_____

_____

Unit 23
Use anytime

Name _____

Just for Fun • World Map

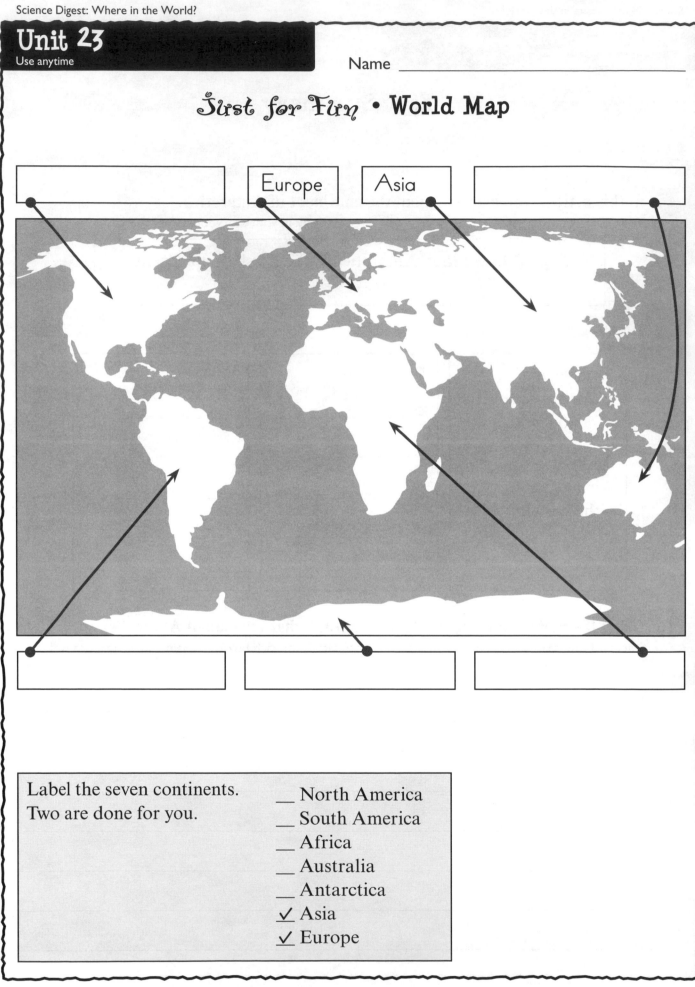

Europe	Asia

Label the seven continents.
Two are done for you.

__ North America
__ South America
__ Africa
__ Australia
__ Antarctica
✓ Asia
✓ Europe

Unit 23 Activity 2
Use after Exercise 2 and What's Black and White and Royalty?

Name _____

Science Digest • Entry 2a

1 **Read your fact summary about Antarctica from Activity 1.**

☐ Does your summary make sense?

☐ Does your paragraph have snazzy words? Look at the word bank. Circle the words you've already used in your paragraph. You may want to add or change a few words in your paragraph.

☐ Copy your summary carefully onto pages 2 and 3 of your Science Digest.

2 **Complete "A Penguin's Calendar" on pages 4 and 5 of your Science Digest.**

☐ Cut out the pictures.

☐ Place and glue them in the correct sequence.

Snazzy Word Bank
harshest
unique
temperature
fascinate
ecosystem
vast
impressive
freezing

A Penguin's Calendar • Entry 2b

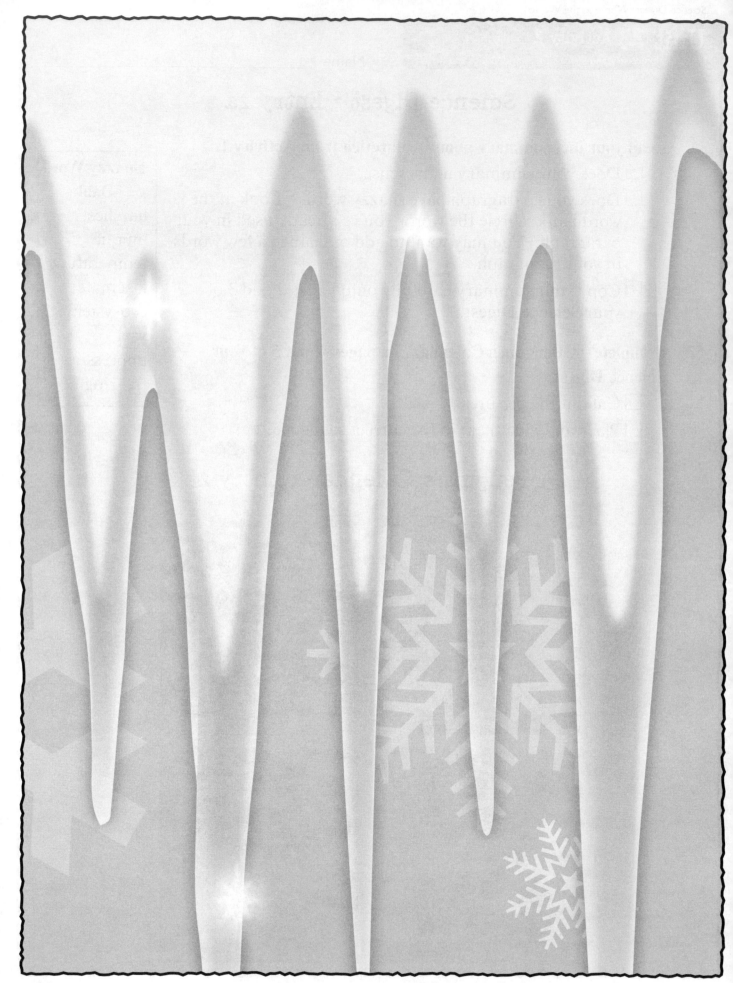

Unit 23 Activity 3
Use after Exercise 3; and Thor, Emily, and the
Little Successor, Chapters 2 and 3

Name _____

Main Idea and Supporting Details

Emperor penguins survive the freezing cold with layers and layers of protection. First, they have a layer of feathers. Under the feathers is a layer of air. Finally, under the air is a layer of skin called blubber. These layers keep heat in and cold out.

1 **What is this paragraph about?**

_____

2 **Supporting Details**
List the details.

Main Idea:

• _____

_____

• _____

_____

• _____

_____

Name _____

Passage Reading Fluency

1. Practice these words:

vacant	brilliant	expedition	inventor	practical

2. Read the story 2 times. Cross out a lightbulb each time you read the story.

Ben's E-Mail

Dear Maya and Ana,   4

Good news! We are on our way to Antarctica. Dad got a job   17
working with some scientists who are studying penguins. We can't wait   28
to go. The expedition leaves soon.   34

Even better news! When we get back, we're moving back to the   46
Bronx. Dad says our old apartment is going to be vacant. So, guess   59
what? We will be neighbors again. I hope we can be in the same class   74
again.   75

Oh, by the way, I read *Thomas Edison: A Brilliant Inventor.* He   87
invented the first practical lightbulb and lit up a town to prove how   100
well it worked. He invented the first movies and the   110
first machine to record sound. Was he cool, or   119
what? I guess my name is okay.   126

Your friend,   128

Benjamin Franklin Thomas Edison Wright   133

3. Set a timer and see how far you can read in one minute.
   Then cross out the timer.

Unit 23 Activity 5

Use after Exercise 4; and Thor, Emily, and the Little
Successor, Chapters 3 and 4

Name _____

Vocabulary Log

Word	Definition—In your own words	Sentence	Picture
harsh	Something that is harsh is very difficult or hard to survive in.	The wind was harsh. My umbrella blew inside out and I could barely walk.	
unsettled	Someone who is unsettled is . . . _____ _____	_____ _____ _____	
vast	Something that _____ _____ _____	_____ _____ _____	
unique	_____ _____ _____	_____ _____ _____	

Unit 23 Activity 6a

Use after Exercise 4; and Thor, Emily, and the Little
Successor, Chapters 3 and 4

Name _____

Thor and Emily's Calendar

You may wish to look back in your storybook on pages 30–50 or in your Science Digest on pages 4 and 5.

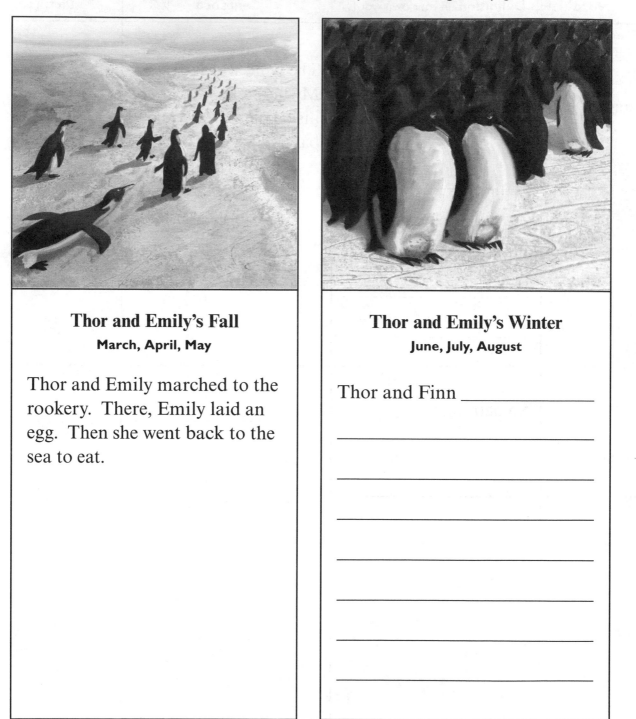

Thor and Emily's Fall
March, April, May

Thor and Emily marched to the rookery. There, Emily laid an egg. Then she went back to the sea to eat.

Thor and Emily's Winter
June, July, August

Thor and Finn _____

_____

_____

_____

_____

_____

_____

_____

continued

Unit 23 Activity 6b

Use after Exercise 4; and Thor, Emily, and the Little
Successor, Chapters 3 and 4

Name _____

Thor and Emily's Calendar

You may wish to look back in your storybook on pages 30–50 or in your Science Digest on pages 4 and 5.

Thor and Emily's Spring
September, October, November

In the spring, Emily and the other mother penguins returned. Emily and Thor found each other. Emily, Thor, and the Little Successor were a happy family!

Thor and Emily's Summer
December, January, February

The story doesn't say what happened in the summer, but Thor, Emily, and the Little Successor did what all emperor penguins do. Explain what they did in the summer. You may wish to look at pages 4 and 5 in your Science Digest.

Emily, Thor, and the Little

Successor _____

_____

_____

_____

_____

_____

Name _____

Passage Comprehension
Layers of the Rain Forest

1 Tropical rain forests are the . . .

    ○ driest places on Earth.   ○ wettest places on Earth.

2 Look at the map in your storybook on page 57. The map shows that tropical rain forests grow near the equator. List three of the continents that have rain forests.

    a. _____

    b. _____

    c. _____

3 Tropical rain forests have four layers. Use the chart to describe each layer and the kind of animals you might find in that layer of the rain forest.

Layer	Plants	Animals
Emergent	• some trees more than _____ feet tall	• bats • _____
Canopy	• trees are _____ feet tall • very thick layer	• monkeys • _____
Understory	• trees are _____ feet tall	• insects • _____
Forest Floor	• little plant life • _____	• deer • _____ • _____

Unit 23 Activity 8
Use after Exercise 7 and Tropical Rain Forest, Chapter 2

Name _____

Passage Comprehension • Rain Forest Animals
Layers of the Rain Forest

1 **Read the sentences and check the box for *True* or *False*.**

Harpy Eagle

	True Yes, it's true.	False No, it's not true.
The harpy eagle is an herbivore.		
The harpy eagle is very clumsy. It bumps into trees.		
The harpy eagle has big strong claws called talons.		

Howler Monkey

	True Yes, it's true.	False No, it's not true.
The howler monkey lives in the understory.		
The howler monkey is an herbivore.		
The howler monkey eats harpy eagles.		

2 **Write a caption for each picture.**

_____ _____

_____ _____

_____ _____

_____ _____

Unit 23 Activity 9
Use after Exercise 7 and before Miss Tam's Corner

Name _____

Crossword Puzzle
Miss Tam's Corner

Fill in the blanks using words from the word bank. Use the words to complete the crossword puzzle. Cross out the words from the word bank as you use them.

Down

1. We save our old newspapers and _____ them.

2. We _____ our shopping bag.

3. I am going to _____ my use of water by taking shorter showers.

Across

4. Earth is a _____ planet.

5. We want to _____ the rain forest trees so animals have a place to live.

6. The Children's Eternal Rain Forest is an _____ plan.

Word Bank

marvelous
reduce
exceptional
reuse
conserve
recycle

Dear Judy Moody
Letters and Notes for Your Not-So-Moody Friend

| The Many Faces of Judy Moody | Entry 1b **Crazy Strips Contest** | Entry 2b **Batty for Banana Peels** | Entry 3b **A Mr. Rubbish Mood** |

Entry 11b **The Winking Disease**

Entry 10b **Batty for Bottles**

Mood Chart

happy

proud

worried

excited

moody

jealous

upset

angry

Entry 4b **Pigtoes, Pumas, and Pimplebacks**

Entry 5b **Beetle Emergency**

Entry 9b **Project P.E.N.C.I.L.**   **Entry 8b** **Batty for Band-Aids**   **Entry 7b** **Luna Two**   **Entry 6b** **Pond Scum**

Teachers: If you are using the Activity Book, tear out and staple pages 47–58 to make a separate Book Journal.

Entry 1a

Chapter 1

Crazy Strips Contest

Date _____

Dear Judy Moody,

    My name is _____

I am _____ years old. I attend _____

_____

I just started reading your book *Judy Moody Saves the World!* After reading Chapter 1, I think this book is going to be _____

    One thing I liked about Chapter 1 was _____

_____

    One thing I didn't like about Chapter 1 was _____

_____

                 Your Not-So-Moody Friend,

               _____

Now turn to the front cover and complete Entry 1b by drawing a face that shows Judy's mood at the end of this chapter.

Entry 2a

Chapter 2
Batty for Banana Peels

Try to use a snazzy word in your letter:

endangered

environment

compost

heal

recycle

Date _____

Dear Judy Moody,

    I see that your brother, Stink, came up with a design for the Crazy Strips Contest. I think his design is cool because _____

_____

    I also like the ideas your class came up with to save the world. I think the best idea is _____

_____

_____

              Your Not-So-Moody Friend,

              _____

P.S. I _____ your design for the Crazy

      liked   didn't like

Strips contest because _____

_____

_____

Now turn to the front cover and complete Entry 2b by drawing a face that shows Judy's mood at the end of this chapter.

Entry 3a

Chapter 3
A Mr. Rubbish Mood

Date _____

Dear Judy Moody,

    You sure found a lot of things in your home that come from the rain forest. Here's a list of things in my house that come from the rain forest.

- _____
- _____
- _____
- _____
- _____
- _____

    To help protect our environment, I think we should . . .

_____

_____

_____

        Your Not-So-Moody Friend,

_____

Tip

You might want to look back in your storybook to help you complete your list of things that come from the rain forest.

Now turn to the front cover and complete Entry 3b by drawing a face that shows Judy's mood at the end of this chapter.

Entry 4a

Chapter 4

Pigtoes, Pumas, and Pimplebacks

Endangered Animals

Choose an animal from this list or write about another endangered animal that you know about.

- **koala**
- **tiger**
- **orangutan**
- **African elephant**
- **sea otter**
- **humpback whale**
- **giant panda**
- **mountain gorilla**
- **cheetah**
- **green turtle**

Date _____

Dear Judy Moody,

I think it's fun that everyone in your class is adopting an endangered animal. If I were writing a report about an endangered species, I would want to write about

_____

Here are some questions I would want to answer.

• Where do _____

_____

• How many _____

_____

• Why _____

_____

• What _____

_____

I could find information for my report in these places:

• _____

• _____

Your Not-So-Moody Friend,

_____

Now turn to the front cover and complete Entry 4b by drawing a face that shows Judy's mood at the end of this chapter.

Entry
5a

Chapter 5

Beetle Emergency

Date _____

Dear Judy Moody,

How is your Project Recycle going? I was trying to think of things that I could recycle or reuse. Here is what I came up with. Each item starts with a letter in the word "recycle."

R _____

E _____

C _____

Y _____

C _____

L _____

E _____

Your Not-So-Moody Friend,

_____

- cans
- cats
- cardboard
- elephants
- empty bottles
- encyclopedias
- lamps
- letters
- lions
- rhinos
- rubber bands
- yarn
- yellow ducks
- rugs
- yo-yos

Now turn to the front cover and complete Entry 5b by drawing a face that shows Judy's mood at the end of this chapter.

Entry 6a

Chapter 6

Pond Scum

Date _____

Dear Judy Moody,

Stink was sure upset with you for setting Toady free.

I think he is going to miss Toady.

This is my opinion about the whole mess. I think

_____

_____

_____

Your Not-So-Moody Friend,

_____

P.S. Here is a picture of Toady and how I think he feels

now that he has been set free.

Now turn to the front cover and complete Entry 6b by drawing a face that shows Judy's mood at the end of this chapter.

Entry 7a

Chapter 7

Luna Two

Date _____

Dear Judy Moody,

    I know you went up into the tree because your family was mad at you. I have always wondered what it would be like to live in a tree.

    Here are some questions I have for you:

• How did you get up the tree?

• Why _____

_____

• When _____

_____

• Who _____

_____

Your Not-So-Moody Friend,

_____

Now turn to the front cover and complete Entry 7b by drawing a face that shows Judy's mood at the end of this chapter.

Chapter 8

Batty for Band-Aids

Entry 8a

Date _____

Dear Judy Moody,

I guess you are upset because Stink won the Crazy

Strips Contest. If I had a little brother who won a contest

that I entered too, it _____

_____

_____

_____

_____

_____

_____

                            Your Not-So-Moody Friend,

                            _____

Try to use a snazzy word in your letter:

mood

original

annoy

green with envy

creative

Now turn to the front cover and complete Entry 8b by drawing a face that shows Judy's mood at the end of this chapter.

Entry 9a

Chapter 9

Project P.E.N.C.I.L.

Date _____

Dear Judy Moody,

I thought your idea about not using pencils was

_____

_____

Your idea about collecting bottles to raise money for

the Children's Eternal Rain Forest was _____

_____

_____

If I could help the Children's Eternal Rain Forest, this

is what I would do. I would _____

_____

_____

Your Not-So-Moody Friend,

_____

Try to use a snazzy word in your letter:

original

awesome

splendid

creative

brilliant

good cause

environment

endangered species

Now turn to the front cover and complete Entry 9b by drawing a face that shows Judy's mood at the end of this chapter.

56

Entry 10a

Chapter 10

Batty for Bottles

Try to use a snazzy word in your letter:

heroine

stick your neck out

mood

determined

stubborn

Date _____

Dear Judy Moody,

    I think the author, Megan McDonald, did _____

_____ job creating you.

    I know why Ms. McDonald decided to call you Judy

Moody. It is because _____

_____

    One thing I like about you is _____

_____

_____

    I wish you would _____

_____

                 Your Not-So-Moody Friend,

                 _____

Now turn to the front cover and complete Entry 10b by drawing a face that shows Judy's mood at the end of this chapter.

Entry 11a

Chapter 11

The Winking Disease

Date _____

Dear Judy Moody,

    We finished your book today. I think your book is

_____

_____

    I am going to tell my friends that they _____

                                           should   should not

read *Judy Moody Saves the World!* because _____

_____

_____

_____

_____

                         Your Not-So-Moody Friend,

                         _____

Now turn to the front cover and complete Entry 11b by drawing a face that shows Judy's mood at the end of this chapter.

58

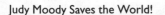

Unit 24 Activity 1
Use after Exercise 1 and Chapter 1

Name _____

Story Comprehension
Crazy Strips Contest

1 **At the beginning of the chapter, the author introduced us to Judy Moody. Judy Moody . . .** Check all correct descriptions.

__ is the main character. __ likes bats.

__ has a brother named Stink. __ wears beads in her hair.

2 **Judy and her brother, Stink, decided to enter the Crazy Strips bandage contest. The top winner would win Rollerblades and . . .**

○ a trip to the Great Barrier Reef.

○ would have their design on a Crazy Strip bandage.

3 **Draw a picture of Stink's Crazy Strip design. Write his theme in the center.**

4 **Cause and Effect: At the end of Chapter 1, Judy was in a bad mood. Why?**

Action/Cause	Outcome/Effect
Judy could not _____ _____ _____	Judy Moody was in a bad mood.

Name _____

Story Comprehension
Batty for Banana Peels

1 **Judy Moody's class is studying** _____

    ◯ the universe   ◯ the environment   ◯ Crazy Strips

2 **Write three ideas Judy Moody's class came up with to help save the Earth.**
If you need to, look back in your storybook on pages 18 and 19.

    Topic: Ways to help save the Earth

    Idea 1: _____

    Idea 2: _____

    Idea 3: _____

3 **Judy Moody asked her friend Rocky to come over to her house to eat bananas. She was going to start to heal the world by . . .**

    ◯ feeding banana peels to the dogs.

    ◯ turning banana peels into compost.

4 **Draw a picture of Judy's Crazy Strip design. Write her theme across the bottom of the bandage.**

Name _____

Vocabulary Log

Word	Definition	Sentence	Picture
outrageous	Something that is _____ _____ _____	_____ _____ _____ _____	
moody	Someone who is moody _____ _____	_____ _____ _____ _____	
mood	A mood is _____ _____ _____ _____	At the end of Chapter 3, Judy thinks her family doesn't understand her. This put Judy in a _____	
creative	Someone who is creative _____ _____ _____	_____ _____ _____	

Unit 24 Activity 4

Name _____

Story Comprehension

Pigtoes, Pumas, and Pimplebacks

1 **Each student in Judy Moody's class is adopting an endangered animal to study. Which endangered animal is Judy adopting and studying?**

○ the elderberry longhorn beetle

○ the marilyn barilyn crazy beetle

○ the northeast beach tiger beetle

2 **Mr. Todd told the class to find information about their endangered animals.** Check the places he suggested they look.

__ the library   __ the museum

__ the Web on the computer   __ their pockets

3 **Did Judy find information about her beetle?**   yes   no

4 **At the end of the chapter, Judy Moody said, "My grade in Science is endangered, too." What do you think she meant by this?**

_____

_____

_____

5 **Cause and Effect: What kind of mood do you think Judy was in at the end of the chapter?**

Action/Cause	Outcome/Effect
Judy Moody was worried about her grade in Science.	Judy Moody's mood was . . . ○ happy. ○ excited. ○ unsettled.

Unit 24 Activity 5
Use after Exercise 5 and Chapter 5

Name _____

Story Comprehension
Beetle Emergency

1 Frank "saved the day" for Judy. Explain how.

_____

_____

_____

_____

2 Judy learned some facts about the northeast beach tiger beetle from Frank's stamp. Read each sentence and check the box for true or false.

The northeast beach tiger beetle is . . .	**True** Yes, it's true.	**False** No, it's not true.
• found along sandy beaches in Virginia.		
• endangered because of temperature changes and lack of food.		
• endangered by changes in its habitat.		
• also known as *Cicindela dorsalis dorsalis*.		

3 Cause and Effect: Judy was in a good mood at the end of this chapter. Why?

Action/Cause	Outcome/Effect
Judy Moody made _____ _____ _____	Judy was in a good mood. She was happy.

Name _____

Maze Reading

When you come to the words between the parentheses, circle the word that makes the most sense in the paragraph. Then reread the paragraph to see if it makes sense.

Endangered Species

An endangered species is a plant or animal that is in danger of becoming extinct. When a species is endangered, there (is, look, extinct) still time to save it. A (never, northeast, shallow) beach tiger beetle is an endangered (insect, mammal, from). A star cactus is an endangered (colorful, poodle, plant).

People can help endangered plants and (oxygen, animals, moody) by working to protect their habitats.

Story Comprehension
Pond Scum

1 **In "Pond Scum," Judy Moody put Toady, Stink's toad and the T. P. Club mascot, back into the pond. Why did she do this?**

She put Toady back in the pond because _____

_____

_____

_____

2 **Judy was in a _____ mood because she thought she was on her way to making the world a better place.**

Unit 24 Activity 7
Use after Exercise 7 and Chapter 7

Name _____

Vocabulary

Choose the best vocabulary word to complete each sentence. Then reread the sentence to see if it makes sense.

1 We can _____ plastic so it can be used again.
  ○ recycle   ○ heal   ○ brag about

2 The _____ tree was over 100 years old.
  ○ mascot   ○ ancient   ○ habitat

3 I had to _____ the loud music so I could sleep.
  ○ ignore   ○ compost   ○ ruin

4 The directions for making the model airplane were _____
  ○ stubborn   ○ complicated   ○ adopted

Story Comprehension
Luna Two

1 **Why did Judy Moody sit in a tree?** (Start with *Judy Moody sat in a tree because . . .*)

_____

_____

_____

2 **Cause and Effect: Why was Judy in a bad mood at the end of the chapter?**

Action/Cause	Outcome/Effect
Stink tricked Judy. He made her think she had won the Crazy Strips contest.	Judy was _____ She was in a _____ mood.

Name _____

Mystery Character

Batty for Band-Aids

1 **Read the sentences and write the name of the mystery character. Next draw a picture of the character in the box.**

I did a report on the northeast beach tiger beetle. I have many moods. **Who am I?** _____	
My bandage design will be printed on Crazy Strips for the month of October. My sister put Toady back into the pond without my permission. **Who am I?** _____	
I am a third-grade teacher. Judy Moody is in my class. We are learning about endangered species. **Who am I?** _____	

2 **My mystery riddle. Write two sentences about yourself.**

_____ _____ _____ **Who am I?** _____	

Unit 24 Activity 9

Name _____

Snazzy Words and Synonyms

Draw a line between the words that mean the same or almost the same thing.

creative •   • use less

outrageous •   • said you did
                                          something wrong

conserve •   • imaginative

confessed •   • shocking

Story Comprehension and Snazzy Words
Project P.E.N.C.I.L.

Fill in each blank with a snazzy word that makes the sentence more sophisticated or grown-up.

1 **Judy had an _____ idea for saving the rain forest.**

2 **Judy wanted to _____ trees, so she hid everyone's pencils.**

3 **Mr. Todd thought Judy's idea was _____ but not practical.**

4 **Judy Moody _____ to taking the pencils.
Then she had a brilliant idea to send money to the Children's Rain Forest.**

5 **Cause and Effect: Judy was in the best mood ever at the end of this chapter.
Why?**

Action/Cause	Outcome/Effect
Judy Moody _____ _____ _____	Judy was in the best mood ever.

Name _____

Passage Reading Fluency

1. Practice these words:

orangutans (uh-rang-uh-tans)	50,000	20,000	Asia

2. Read the story 2 times. Cross out an orangutan each time you read the story.

Orangutans

Orangutans are friendly apes that live in the rain forests of Asia.   12
Sadly, these fascinating creatures are endangered. Fifteen years ago,   21
there were 50,000 orangutans left in the world. Now, there are only   33
about 20,000.   35

Orangutans are very intelligent animals. In the wild, these apes   45
have been seen making simple tools to scratch themselves. Orangutans   55
also use huge leaves to protect themselves from the sun and rain—   67
orangutan umbrellas! Some orangutans even wipe leftover food from   76
their chins with leaves—orangutan napkins!   82

Orangutans are endangered because they are losing their habitat.   91
Much of their forest home has already been cut down. Sadly, mother   103
orangutans are also sometimes killed by humans. These people are   113
called poachers. Poachers kill mother orangutans so they can sell their   124
babies for pets.   127

Some people think that wild orangutans could become extinct in as   138
little as five years. Many people are working to save   148
the orangutans. They are trying to protect   155
the rain forests and put poachers in jail.   163

3. Set a timer and see how far you can read in one minute.
   Then cross out the timer.

Name _____

Locating Information • Fact Summary
Orangutans

1 **There is more than one main idea in Activity 10. Write facts that tell why orangutans are endangered.** If you need to, look in your Comprehension and Skill Activity 10.

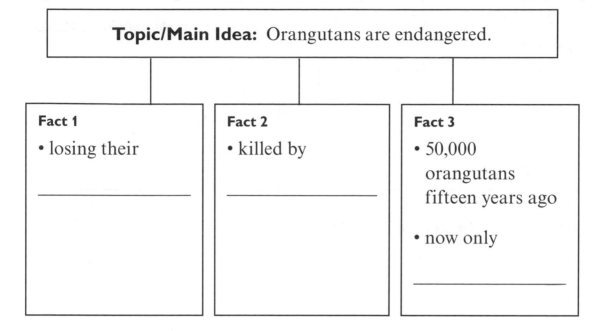

Topic/Main Idea: Orangutans are endangered.

Fact 1
• losing their

_____

Fact 2
• killed by

_____

Fact 3
• 50,000 orangutans fifteen years ago

• now only

_____

2 **Using the facts you listed above, write a paragraph that tells why orangutans are endangered.** (Start with *Orangutans are endangered because . . .*)

_____

_____

_____

_____

_____

_____

Name _____

Story Comprehension
The Winking Disease

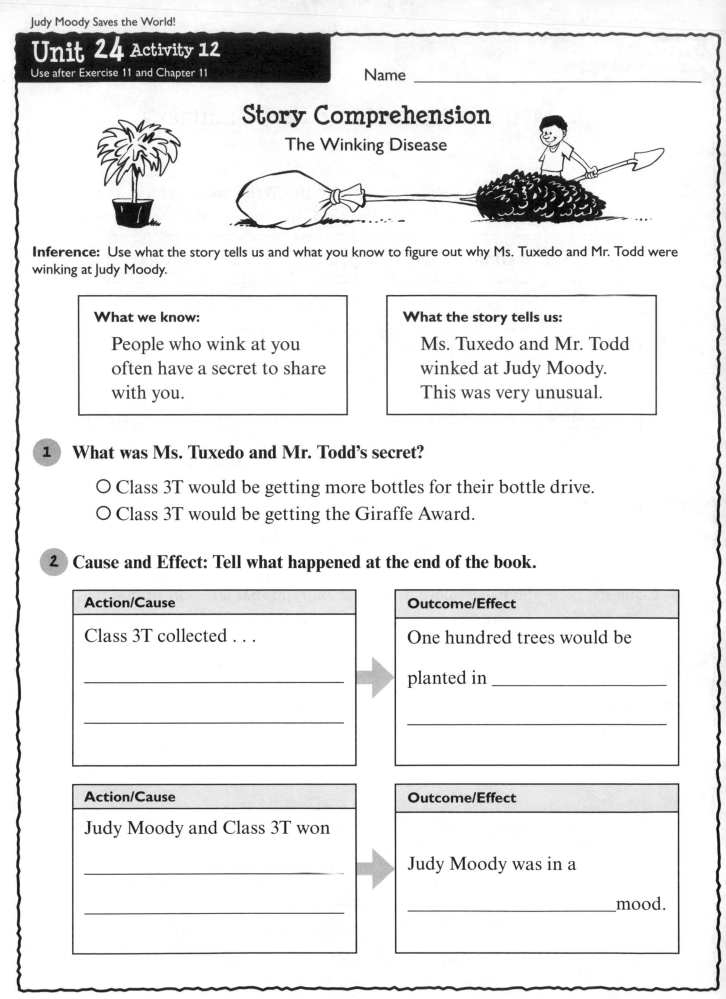

Inference: Use what the story tells us and what you know to figure out why Ms. Tuxedo and Mr. Todd were winking at Judy Moody.

What we know:	**What the story tells us:**
People who wink at you often have a secret to share with you.	Ms. Tuxedo and Mr. Todd winked at Judy Moody. This was very unusual.

1 **What was Ms. Tuxedo and Mr. Todd's secret?**

○ Class 3T would be getting more bottles for their bottle drive.

○ Class 3T would be getting the Giraffe Award.

2 **Cause and Effect: Tell what happened at the end of the book.**

Action/Cause
Class 3T collected . . .   _____   _____

Outcome/Effect
One hundred trees would be   planted in _____   _____

Action/Cause
Judy Moody and Class 3T won   _____   _____

Outcome/Effect
Judy Moody was in a   _____ mood.

Main Character: Dink Duncan

Author: Ron Roy

by Dink and Kid Detective _____

Case Log • Sir Winston's E-Mail

⊘	🗑	↩	↩↩	➡	🖨
Delete	Junk	Reply	Reply All		Print

From: Sir Winston, Master Detective
              President, Detective Club
Subject: The Case of the Absent Author
Date: July 16, 2008, 11:30 a.m.
To: Dink

Dear Dink,

I received your e-mail.

I am happy to serve as your advisor on this case.

First piece of advice: Be sure to start your case log.
There is no case too big or small. Remember that a
good detective always asks questions and takes notes.

Looking forward to hearing from you again,

Sir Winston
Dog Detective

Case Log

The Case of the Absent Author

A good detective always takes notes and asks questions.

1. Missing: _____

2. I (Dink) wrote to _____

   _____

   I invited him to _____

   _____

3. Wallis Wallace wrote to Dink. Letter said:

   _____

   _____

4. Scheduled to sign autographs:

   Where: _____

   When: _____

5. Problem: _____

   _____

6. Question I have: _____

   _____

   _____

   _____

Entry
2
Chapter 3

Case Log

Case Notes: AA (p.2)

Suspicions:

1. Officer Fallon thinks: _____

2. Josh thinks: _____

Clues from Wallis's Letter to Mavis Green:

3. Wallis Wallace agrees to meet Mavis _____

_____

4. Wallis Wallace sounds worried because _____

_____

5. Draw what's at the top of each letter.

A good detective always draws illustrations of clues.

Top Of Letter To Mavis	**Top Of Letter To Dink**

Entry
3
Chapter 4

Case Log

Case Notes: AA (p.3)

Call to Airport from Ellie's Diner:

1. Wallis Wallace on _____

2. Flight: _____

Interview:

1. Taxi Driver: _____

2. Picked up Wallis Wallace

3. Time: _____

4. Maureen's Description of Wallis Wallace

   • _____

   • _____

   • _____

   • _____

5. Dropped Wallis Wallace off

   Where: _____

Question I have:

_____

_____

A good detective follows every lead.

E-Mail to Sir Winston

Delete   Junk   Reply   Reply All   Print

From: Dink, Member of Detective Club
Subject: Update on the The Case of the Absent Author
Date: July 16, 2008, 1:00 p.m.
To: Sir Winston

Dear Sir Winston,

This is what we've learned so far.
From Wallis Wallace's letters:

- Concerned about being _____

From taxi driver Maureen _____

- Wallis was dropped off at _____

From hotel clerk Mr. _____

- Wallis checked in at _____ into room _____

- Wallis still in room, but doesn't answer _____

Other clues: Signature in hotel register is the _____ as other Wallis Wallace signatures.

What do you think?
- Was the author kidnapped?
- Did the author get lost?
- Did the author decide he didn't want to sign autographs?

My suspicion: I think Wallis Wallace _____

_____

Yours truly, Dink

Entry
5
Chapter 6

Case Log

Case Notes: AA (p.4)

Josh's Suspect:

Kidnapper is _____

Interview:

Maid: _____

Where: _____

Room 303: No one slept there

Bed: _____

Towels: _____

Sign on Door: _____

My (Dink's) Conclusion:

Wallis Wallace walked into Shangri-la last night and

_____

_____

_____

You can solve this case. A detective club member never gives up!

Entry
6
Chapter 7

Case Log

> A good detective club member always eats lunch.

Case Notes: AA (p.5)

While eating lunch, Josh discussed his suspicions.

Josh's Suspects: The kidnapper is . . .

- Book Nook owner: _____

- Taxi driver: _____

- Hotel clerk: _____

- _____ Olivia Nugent

Ruth Rose said we should review what we know about

the missing author.

What We Know About Wallis Wallace:

I THINK . . . the author must be . . .

O wealthy and like animals.

O poor.

O a man.

- Favorite color _____

- Lives in castle called _____

  _____

- Donates money to favorite cause: _____

  _____

Something Weird at the Shangri-la Hotel:

302: Do not disturb sign

303: _____

Entry 7 Chapters 8 and 9

Case Log

Case Notes: AA (p.6)

Back at the Shangri-la:

- Mavis Green waiting at the hotel

- Wearing a scarf with _____

- Asked Mr. Linkletter _____

  _____

- Heard _____

- Room 302, heard _____

- Found in 302: _____

  _____

Ruth Rose's Suspicion:

- Ruth thinks Mavis Green is _____

What Sir Winston and I think:

_____

_____

_____

A good detective club member always reviews his or her notes.

Case Log

Case Notes: AA (p.7)

Case Solved!

Mavis Green is _____

Important Clues:

- MM on scarf is really _____

- Lives in Moose Manor

- _____ on side of bag

- Favorite color: _____

- Pretend name: Mavis _____

- Favorite ice cream: _____

What We Found Out

Wallis Wallace is a woman.

She was doing research in disguise about kid detectives.

She was impressed we solved the case.

Are we perfect or what?

CASE CLOSED!

PERFECT!

Unit 25 Activity 1
Use after Exercise 1 and Chapters 1 and 2

Name _____

Mystery Character
Chapters 1 and 2

1 **Read the sentences and write the name of the mystery character. Next, draw a picture of the character's face.**

I love books. I love reading books written by Wallis Wallace. I wear thick glasses and look nervous all the time.

Who am I? _____

I usually carry around a sketch pad because I love to draw.

Who am I? _____

I love to read books by Wallis Wallace. I have an orange cat, and I love to wear clothes that are the same color.

Who am I? _____

I sign autographs. I am famous, but no one has seen my picture.

Who am I? _____

2 **Write a mystery riddle for the main character of the book.**

_____

_____

_____

Who am I? _____

Unit 25 Activity 2
Use after Exercise 2 and Chapter 3

Name _____

Story Comprehension
Chapter 3

Read the following events from "Itinerary for Wallis Wallace."

1 **Was it on the itinerary?** Read each sentence and check the box for true or false.

Wallis Wallace was to:	True Yes, it's true.	False No, it's not true.
• arrive at Bradley Airport on flight 3132, July 15		
• take the bus to the Green Lawn bowling alley		
• meet driver from Lawrence Taxi Service, July 15		
• drive to Shangri-la Hotel, July 15		
• visit the penguin exhibit at the zoo, July 16		
• sign books at Book Nook 11:00 a.m., July 16		

2 **Dink said that Wallis Wallace disappeared somewhere along the itinerary. Complete Wallis's original plan.**

Airport ➧ _____ ➧ _____ ➧ _____

3 **What was the name of the writer who came to meet Mr. Wallace?**

     ○ Mavis Wallace   ○ Mavis Green   ○ Ruth Green

4 **Check the clues that make you think Dink's letter and Mavis's letter were written by the same person.**

    __ The signatures look the same.

    __ The writer was not excited about signing autographs.

    __ Both letters are written on the same kind of paper.

Unit 25 Activity 3
Use after Exercise 3 and Chapter 4

Name _____

Vocabulary Log • Word Family

Related words are a family. If you know the meaning of one word, you can figure out the meaning of a related word.

Word	Definition	Sentence	Picture
You know the word: **suspicious**	When something is suspicious, you think that something is . . . _____ _____	Officer Fallon thought that letters from Wallis Wallace were _____	
Related word: **suspect**	A suspect is a person who you think did . . . _____ _____	Mr. Paskey was nervous, so Josh thought Mr. Paskey was a _____	
Related word: **suspicion**	A suspicion is a feeling that someone has . . . _____ _____	Josh's suspicion was that Mr. Paskey had	

Unit 25 Activity 4
Use after Exercise 4 and Chapter 5

Name _____

Adjectives and Alphabetical Order

1. Fill in the missing letters of the alphabet.

2. Make up the titles of your own A to Z Mysteries. The titles for <u>A</u>, <u>C</u>, <u>I</u>, <u>K</u>, <u>Q</u>, <u>R</u>, <u>T</u>, and <u>Y</u> are done for you.
   Each word of the title must begin with the same letter.

	Adjective	Noun • Person, Place or Thing
	Ancient	Arachnid
	Brilliant	
C	Curious	Carnivore
	Discouraged	
	Educated	
F	Frantic	
	Gloomy	
	Harsh	
I	Invisible	Inventor
	Jealous	
K	Kind	Kangaroo
L	Luscious	
	Moody	
	Nocturnal	
O	Ordinary	
	Popular	
Q	Quiet	Queen
R	Rude	Relative
	Suspicious	
T	Terrible	Trickster
U	Unsettled	
	Vast	
W	Wealthy	
XYZ	Yellow	Yarn

Unit 25 Activity 5
Use after Exercise 5 and Chapter 6

Name _____

Story Comprehension • Following Directions
Chapter 6

It's a bird's-eye view!

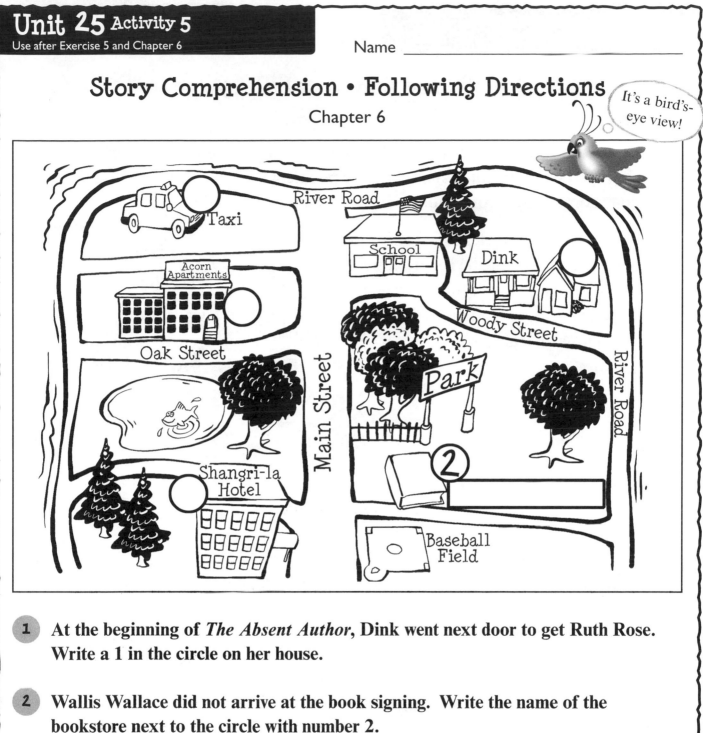

1. At the beginning of *The Absent Author*, Dink went next door to get Ruth Rose. Write a 1 in the circle on her house.

2. Wallis Wallace did not arrive at the book signing. Write the name of the bookstore next to the circle with number 2.

3. A _____ picked up Wallace from the airport. Write a 3 in the circle to show where Dink learned this.

4. Wallis checked in at the _____. Write a 4 to show where he checked in.

5. Livvy told Dink that no one slept in Wallis Wallace's room. Where does Livvy live? Write a 5 in the circle.

Name _____

Genre and Vocabulary
Chapter 7

In a mystery, there is a problem, clues to follow, and often *suspicious* characters. Suspicious characters are people who may or may not have done something wrong, but we suspect them of wrongdoing.

In *The Absent Author*, Wallis Wallace has gone missing. The kid detectives think he may have been kidnapped. In your opinion, who are the suspicious characters?

1 **Dink invited Wallis Wallace to Green Lawn.**

Does this make Dink a suspicious character?   yes   no   maybe

2 **Ruth Rose wears clothes that are all the same color.**

Does this make Ruth Rose a suspicious character?   yes   no   maybe

3 **Mr. Paskey acts nervous.**

Does this make Mr. Paskey a suspicious character?   yes   no   maybe

4 **Mavis Green is a stranger in town.**

Does this make Ms. Green a suspicious character?   yes   no   maybe

5 **Mr. Linkletter, the hotel clerk, was the last to see Wallis Wallace.**

Does this make the clerk a suspicious character?   yes   no   maybe

This is your opinion, so there is no right or wrong answer. Sir Winston and Dink had two "no's," one "maybe," and two "yes's."

Judge _____

COMING SOON! Kids' Choice Awards

You have been selected to be a judge in the *Read Well* Literary Awards. You will have one vote in each of three categories. The categories are: Best Trade Book, Best *Read Well* Book, and Best Main Character.

Begin thinking today. You will vote on _____
Date

Best Trade Book

What is your favorite trade book? _____

Why? _____

_____

_____

Unit 25 Activity 7a
Use after Exercise 7 and Chapters 8 and 9

Judge _____

Best *Read Well* Storybook

Stories
- A Perfect Year
- Eel in the Fish Tank
- A Bird's-Eye View
- People on the Move
- That Kind of Day
- Miss Tam in Africa
- The River Horse

Stories
- Ant Communities
- An Ant With Ideas
- The Lost Treasure
- Sir Henry
- Miss Tam in Hilo
- Tsunami, Wall of Water
- Miss Tam's Scrapbook

Stories
- The Emperor and the Seed
- Stone Soup
- Judith's Story
- Ricardo's Stories
- Fudge

Stories
- Going on a Dino Dig
- A Dinosaur Timeline
- There's a Dinosaur in My Bed
- Sue Goes Missing
- Sue: The Real Story

Stories
- Spider, Spider on the Wall
- Fun With Rhymes
- Centipede and Grandmother Spider
- The War Between Birds and Mammals
- Incredible Flying Machine
- A Bat's Life

Stories
- Snapshots of the American West
- The Cowboy Trail
- The Tall Tale of Pecos Bill
- The Tall Tale of Slue-Foot Sue
- The Ballad of Pecos Bill and Slue-Foot Sue

Articles
- Links in the Chain
- From Grass to Meatballs
- What's Black and White and Loved by All?
- What's at the Top
- Predators
- 10 Great Reasons to be an Earthworm
- The Garden We Share

Stories
- The Great Barrier Reef
- Miss Tam at the Great Barrier Reef
- Wonders of the Coral Reef
- Pete the Pufferfish
- Miss Tam Goes Home

Stories
- The 16th President
- Changing the Face of History

Articles
- Antarctica!
- What's Black and White and Royalty?
- Thor, Emily, and the Little Successor
- The Tropical Rain Forest
- Miss Tam's Corner

Unit 25 Activity 7b
Use after Exercise 7 and Chapters 8 and 9

Name _____

Best *Read Well* Storybook

Critic's Corner: In My Opinion

by _____

★　★　★　★　★

Topic/Main Idea: The best of the *Read Well* storybooks was

_____

_____

Supporting Details:

Why

_____   _____   _____

_____   _____   _____

_____   _____   _____

_____   _____   _____

In my opinion, _____

_____

_____

_____

_____

Unit 25 Activity 8a
Use after Exercise 8 and Chapter 10

Judge _____

Best Main Character(s)

Maya and Ben	**Miss Tam**	**Arthur**	**Antonia Ant**	**Sir Henry**
Jun	**Sir Winston**	**Jack and Annie**	**Pecos Bill**	**Professor Worm**
Pete the Pufferfish	**Flat Stanley**	**Judy Moody**	**Dink**	

First Choice _____

Second Choice _____

Unit 25 Activity 8b
Use after Exercise 8 and Chapter 10

Judge _____

Final Secret Ballot

Category	Ballot
Best Trade Book (See page 85, Activity 6b)	My choice for best trade book is: _____
Best _Read Well_ Book	My choice for best _Read Well_ storybook is: ☐ Our World, Our Home ☐ Communities ☐ From Generation to Generation ☐ All About Dinosaurs ☐ Spiders and Bats ☐ Young America ☐ Science Digest: Food Chains ☐ The Reef ☐ A Great Man ☐ Science Digest: Where in the World?
Best Main Character	My choice for best main character is: ☐ Maya and Ben ☐ Jack and Annie ☐ Miss Tam ☐ Pecos Bill ☐ Arthur ☐ Professor Worm ☐ Antonia Ant ☐ Pete the Pufferfish ☐ Sir Henry ☐ Flat Stanley ☐ Jun ☐ Judy Moody ☐ Sir Winston ☐ Dink

Unit 25
Use anytime

Name _____

Just for Fun • Read Well Literary Award

Draw a picture of your favorite main character on the trophy. Then complete the sentence that tells who your main character is, and explain why that's your favorite character.

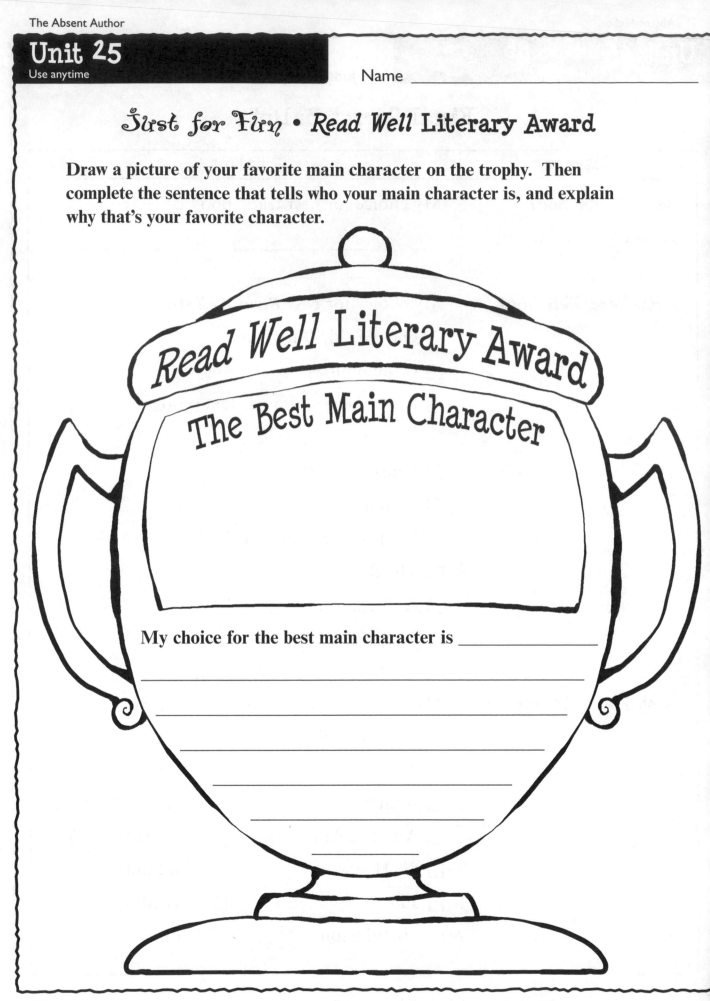

Read Well Literary Award

The Best Main Character

My choice for the best main character is _____

_____

_____

_____

_____

_____

Name _____

Date _____

Helen Keller

Note
• Before beginning the assessment, have students read the title.
  Have students read the warm-up words in the box on the next page.
• Then have students complete the assessment on their own.

WARM-UP

graduate	college	communicate

Someone who cannot see is blind.
Someone who cannot hear is deaf.

Helen Keller

Helen Keller was born in a sleepy little town in the South. When she was born, Helen could hear and see like other children. Helen and her parents were very happy.

When Helen was a year and a half old, she became very sick. The doctor wasn't sure if Helen would live. Helen got well, but she couldn't see or hear.

For many years, Helen lived in a dark and silent world. Then Helen's parents hired a teacher named Annie. Annie knew how to talk with her fingers. Annie taught Helen how to finger spell. For the first time in many years, Helen could communicate. She learned how to read and write. She became the first deaf and blind person to graduate from college.

Helen wanted to help blind people. She wrote articles about how to prevent blindness. Helen wrote books about her life. The books helped people understand what it was like to be deaf and blind.

Helen was an inspiring person. She spoke with people all over the world. She went to the White House. She met artists, actors, and musicians. Helen made a difference in the world. She helped change the way deaf and blind children were treated. She gave people hope.

continued

CHARACTERIZATION, WEB

1 Complete the web by writing words that describe Helen Keller.

Helen Keller

(Bonus)

CHARACTERIZATION, WRITTTEN RESPONSE

2 Describe Helen Keller. Write at least two sentences.

_____

_____

_____

_____

_____

VOCABULARY—INSPIRING

3 Helen was an *inspiring* person. Check two things that made Helen *inspiring*.

___ Helen had a teacher named Annie.

___ Helen became the first deaf and blind person to graduate from college.

___ Helen wrote books and talked with people all over the world.

___ Helen got very sick when she was a year and a half old.

Turn the page.

CAUSE AND EFFECT, CHART

4 **Complete the information about Helen Keller.**

When something happens, it often makes something else happen.

Cause • Event		Effect • What Happened?
When Helen was a year and a half old, she became very sick.	→	Helen got well, but_____ _____
Helen learned how to finger spell.	→	Helen could _____ _____
Helen learned how to read and write.	→	Helen _____ _____

ASKING QUESTIONS

5 **If you could meet Helen Keller, what would you ask her? Write two questions.**

_____

_____

_____

_____

SCORING   Date _____

Characterization, Web ____ /1	Characterization, Written Response ____ /2	Vocabulary ____ /2
Cause and Effect ____ /3	Asking Questions ____ /2	Total ____ /10

Teachers: If you wish to keep a cumulative record of student assessment scores, see the *Assessment Manual*.

Name _____

Date _____

Ruth Wakefield, Inventor

Note

- Before beginning the assessment, have students read the title.
  Have students read the warm-up words in the box on the next page.
- Then have students complete the assessment on their own.

WARM-UP

Toll House Inn	Ruth Wakefield	chocolate	company

Ruth Wakefield, Inventor

What is your favorite cookie? Many people think chocolate chip cookies are the best. They were invented almost 100 years ago by Ruth Wakefield. Even cookies have to be invented!

In 1930, Ruth and her husband bought an old house. It was more than 200 years old. In the 1700s, travelers had stopped at the old house to rest. It was called a toll house. The Wakefields turned the house into a place to eat. They called it the Toll House Inn.

One day Ruth was baking cookies for the inn. She ran out of chocolate powder. This didn't stop Ruth. She broke up a chocolate bar. Then she put the small pieces in the cookie batter. Ruth baked the cookies. She thought the small brown chips would melt together. To her surprise, they didn't. The baked cookies still had chunks of candy in them. She called her new cookies "Toll House Crunch Cookies." People loved them.

A candy company found out about Ruth's cookies. They began selling the chocolate chips. Ruth let the company print her recipe. In return, they gave her free chocolate for the rest of her life!

VOCABULARY—INVENTOR

1 **What made Ruth Wakefield an *inventor*?**

    ○ She found a new way to make cookies.

    ○ She liked chocolate.

    ○ She ran the Toll House Inn.

continued

SEQUENCE OF EVENTS, CHART

2 **Fill in the chart to show the chain of events in the invention of the chocolate chip cookie.**

RETELL, WRITTEN

3 **Using your list of events, write about the invention of the chocolate chip cookie.**

First Event Ruth Wakefield and her husband _____ _____ _____	First, _____ _____ _____ _____
Next Event One day, she ran out of chocolate powder _____ _____ _____	Then, _____ _____ _____ _____
Next Event The chocolate pieces didn't _____ Ruth had invented _____ _____ _____	Next, _____ _____ _____ _____
Conclusion Ruth's recipe was _____ _____ _____ _____	Finally, _____ _____ _____ _____

Turn the page.

VOCABULARY

4 When Ruth Wakefield ran out of powdered chocolate, she used chocolate pieces instead. She used her imagination and thought of a new thing.
She was . . .

○ discouraged.

○ unpopular.

○ creative.

✓ Check and Correct

Reread your answers.

Do your answers make sense? ☐

Do you have a capital at the beginning of each sentence and a period at the end? ☐

Did you use your best handwriting? ☐

SCORING   Date _____

| Vocabulary ___ /1 | Sequence of Events, Chart ___ /4 | Retell ___ /4 |
| Vocabulary ___ /1 | | Total ___ /10 |

Teachers: If you wish to keep a cumulative record of student assessment scores, see the *Assessment Manual*.

Name _____

Date _____

Antarctica Through the Winter

Note
- Before beginning the assessment, have students read the title.
  Have students read the warm-up words in the box on the next page.
- Then have students complete the assessment on their own.

WARM-UP

scientists	blizzard	solve	Antarctica	emperor

Antarctica Through the Winter

Antarctica is the coldest place on Earth. It is frozen all year. On a winter's day, it may be 100 degrees below zero. It is also the windiest place on Earth. Winds race across the ice at 200 miles per hour.

Most animals leave for the winter. Only emperor penguins stay. What about people? Some scientists stay through the winter. People who help them also stay. About a thousand people live in Antarctica through the winter.

Winters in Antarctica are hard. Of course, it is freezing. It is also dark. People must wear layers of clothing. They must have the right tools. They must be careful not to get caught in a blizzard.

Once winter arrives, people cannot come and go. Planes can't land. Ships can't cross the ice. There are no stores. When people stay for the winter, they must have everything they need.

Why do people stay? Scientists study the land. They study the ice. They study the air. They learn about the ocean and food chains.

Scientists are doing important work. By studying Antarctica, they are learning how Earth is changing. Scientists are learning how to solve problems. They are learning information that will help keep Earth healthy.

continued

SUPPORTING DETAILS, CHART, VOCABULARY—HARSH

1 **Write facts that support the main idea.**

Main Idea: Winters in Antarctica are *harsh*.

Fact 1	Fact 2	Fact 3
_____	_____	_____
_____	_____	_____
_____	_____	_____
_____	_____	_____

CAUSE AND EFFECT, CHART

2 **When something happens, it often makes something else happen.**

Cause • Event	Effect • What Happened?
It is hard to survive in the Antarctic winter.	_____ _____

DRAWING CONCLUSIONS

3 **Why do emperor penguins stay in Antarctica through the winter?**
Pick the best answer.

○ They like to play on the ice.

○ They have special ways to survive the Antarctic winter.

○ They are not very smart.

Turn the page.

SUPPORTING DETAILS

4 **Check two facts that explain why people cannot come and go during the Antarctic winter.**

_____ Most animals leave.

_____ Ships cannot cross the ice.

_____ People must wear layers of clothing.

_____ Planes cannot land.

MAIN IDEA, INFERENCE

5 **Scientists study Antarctica in the winter so they . . .**

○ can go shopping.

○ can learn information that will help keep the Earth healthy.

○ can rough it.

PERSONAL RESPONSE, WRITTEN

6 **If you were a scientist in Antarctica, would you volunteer to stay for the winter? Use two facts from the passage to explain why.**

I _____ volunteer to stay for the winter because
　　　would　　　　　would not

_____

_____

_____

✓ Check and Correct

Reread your answers.

Do your answers make sense? ☐

Do you have a capital at the beginning of each sentence
　and a period at the end? ☐

Did you use your best handwriting? ☐

SCORING　　　　　　　　　　　　　　Date _____

| Supporting Details, Chart, Vocabulary ___ /3 | Cause and Effect, Chart ___ /1 | Drawing Conclusions ___ /1 |
| Supporting Details ___ /2 | Main Idea, Inference ___ /1 | Personal Response ___ /2 | Total ___ /10 |

Teachers: If you wish to keep a cumulative record of student assessment scores, see the *Assessment Manual*.

Unit 24 Written Assessment
Use after Exercise 12 and Who Am I?

Name _____

Date _____

Rain Forest Predator

Note

- Before beginning the assessment, have students read the title.
  Have students read the warm-up words in the box on the next page.
- Then have students complete the assessment on their own.

WARM-UP

| Pablo | talons | ducked | gracefully | Costa Rica |

Rain Forest Predator

Jane was hiking through the rain forest. Her mom and dad followed closely behind her. Pablo, their guide, walked in front of them all. He turned to the others and whispered, "Keep your eyes open. We're getting close. The nest is in that large tree ahead."

Everyone was trying to be quiet. The only sounds were their soft footsteps and the light rain falling on the leaves. Jane could hardly believe she was in the rain forest. The air was warm and moist. When she looked up, enormous trees towered above her. The tropical rain forest of Costa Rica was an incredible habitat.

Suddenly a huge gray and white bird swooped past overhead. It held a snake in its giant talons. Everyone ducked. It flew to its nest high in the tree and landed gracefully. Jane's dad quietly took out his camera and began to take pictures.

The predator ignored the staring people and started to eat its prey. "I can't wait to tell the kids at home about this!" Jane thought. "A real harpy eagle! They'll be green with envy!"

continued

GOAL, INFERENCE

1 **What tells you Jane and her parents hoped to see a rain forest bird?**

○ Pablo, the guide, told them to watch for the nest in the tree ahead.

○ Pablo, the guide, told them to speak softly.

○ Jane's dad took out his camera.

SETTING, WRITTEN RESPONSE

2 **Describe the rain forest. Write at least two sentences.**

_____

_____

_____

_____

_____

MIDDLE—ACTION

3 **Write what happened in the middle of the story. Write at least two sentences.**

Suddenly, _____

_____

_____

_____

_____

VOCABULARY—PREDATOR

4 **What was the *predator*?**

○ a towering tree

○ a harpy eagle

○ food

Turn the page.

CAUSE AND EFFECT, CHART

5 **When something happens, it often makes something else happen.**

Cause • Event
The huge bird swooped overhead.

Effect • What Happened?
Everyone _____   _____

IDIOMS AND EXPRESSIONS —GREEN WITH ENVY

6 **At the end of the story, Jane said her friends will be *green with envy*. What did Jane mean?**

○ Her friends were very sick and couldn't go with her on this adventure.

○ Her friends will be jealous that she got to go on this adventure.

○ Her friends will be very happy that she got to go on this adventure.

ASKING QUESTIONS

7 **If you saw Jane after her trip to Costa Rica, what would you ask her?**
Write two questions.

_____

_____

_____

_____

✓ Check
and Correct

Do your answers make sense?   ☐
Do you have a capital at the beginning of each sentence
    and a period at the end?   ☐
Did you use your best handwriting?   ☐

SCORING   Date _____

Goal, Inference ___ /1	Setting ___ /2	Middle—Action ___ /2
Vocabulary ___ /1	Cause and Effect, Chart ___ /1	Idioms and Expressions ___ /1
Asking Questions ___ /2		Total ___ /10

Teachers: If you wish to keep a cumulative record of student assessment scores, see the *Assessment Manual*.